iPhone Manual for Beginners

5th Edition

The Perfect iPhone Guide for Seniors, Beginners, & First-time iPhone Users

Covers iPhones: 12, 12 Pro, 12 Pro Max, SE, 11, 11 Pro, 11 Pro Max, XS, XS Max, XR, X, 8, 8 Plus, 7, 7 Plus, 6s, 6s Plus, 6, 6 Plus, 5s, 5c, & 5.

Joe Malacina

An Infinity Guides book
InfinityGuides.com

iPhone Manual for Beginners

Trademarks & Acknowledgements
Every effort has been made by the publisher and the author to show known trademarks as capitalized in this text. No Limit Enterprises, Inc. cannot attest to the accuracy of this information, and use of a term in this text should not be regarded as affecting the validity of any trademark or copyrighted term. iPhone® is a registered trademark of Apple, Inc. All other trademarks are the property of their respective owners. The publisher and the author are not associated with any product or vendor mentioned in this book with the exception of Infinity Guides. *iPhone® Manual for Beginners* is an independent publication and has not been authorized, sponsored, or otherwise approved by Apple, Inc. Other registered trademarks of Apple, Inc. referenced in this book include: iCloud®, iTunes®, iPad®, Mac®, AirDrop®, and others.

Warning & Disclaimer
Every effort has been made to ensure this text is as accurate and complete as possible. This text does not cover every single aspect, nor was it intended to do so. Instead, the text is meant to be a building block for successful learning of the subject matter of this text. No warranty whatsoever is implied. The author and No Limit Enterprises, Inc. shall have neither liability nor responsibility to any person or entity with respect to any losses or damages arising from the information contained in this text.

Contact the Publisher
To contact No Limit Enterprises, Inc. or the author for sales, marketing material, or any commercial purpose, please visit www.nolimitcorp.com, or e-mail info@nolimitcorp.com.

iPhone® Manual for Beginners, 5th Edition

Publisher: No Limit Enterprises, Inc.

Author: Joe Malacina

Print ISBN: 978-1-7342604-3-4

Library of Congress Control Number: 2020952699

Printed in the U.S.A.

About the Author

Joe Malacina is the founder of *InfinityGuides.com*, a beginner's help website that offers books, DVDs, and online courses to help people learn how to use technology. Since 2013, *InfinityGuides.com* has taught hundreds of thousands of people how to use their devices and how to use social media. Prior to authoring numerous how-to books, Malacina operated two popular tech blogs with a combined audience of over one million people that focused on the most popular smartphones and tablets. He has also been a guest speaker at technology and adult education conferences around the United States. His approach for teaching technology devices has focused on stressing the basics to build technological intuition, thus allowing users to become experts at using their devices in a relatively short amount of time. Following the success of his blogs and seminars, Malacina authored his first book, the *iPhone Manual for Beginners (1st Edition),* which was published in 2017 and reached the *InfinityGuides.com's* Best-Seller list within the first week and remained there for over six months. His published works have earned praise from notable tech aficionados, adult and senior organizations, and readers alike, and can be found in households across the United States, Canada, Australia, and the United Kingdom.

Malacina holds an MBA in Finance from the University of Illinois at Chicago and holds a Bachelor of Science in Mechanical Engineering from the same university. He has been profiled and interviewed on numerous radio stations, podcasts, and blogs and is often on a speaking tour in the United States. He lives and works in Lake Villa, IL, United States.

www.joemalacina.com

Also by Joe Malacina

iPad Manual for Beginners: The Perfect iPad Guide for Beginners, Seniors, & First-time iPad Users

Online Safety: The Complete Guide to Being Safe Online

Galaxy S8 Manual for Beginners: The Perfect Galaxy S8 Guide for Beginners, Seniors, & First-time Galaxy Users

Kindle Manual for Beginners: The Perfect Kindle Guide for Beginners, Seniors, & First-time Kindle Users

Fire HD Manual for Beginners: The Complete Guide to using the Fire HD for Beginners, Seniors, & First-time Fire Tablet Users

What's new in the 5th Edition

The 5th edition has been completely updated from the 4th edition to reflect all the changes that have come with the latest software updates. The 5th edition covers all iPhones that run the operating systems iOS 10, iOS 11, iOS 12, iOS 13, and iOS 14 and newer, which includes the iPhone 12, iPhone 12 Pro, iPhone 12 Pro Max, iPhone SE, iPhone 11, iPhone 11 Pro, iPhone 11 Pro Max, iPhone XS, iPhone XS Max, iPhone XR, iPhone X, iPhone 8, iPhone 8 Plus, iPhone 7, iPhone 7 Plus, iPhone 6s, iPhone 6s Plus, iPhone 6, iPhone 6 Plus, iPhone 5s, iPhone 5c, and iPhone 5. In addition, every chapter has been updated to include the new best practices for performing functions and several new tasks have been added that were found to be beneficial to readers. Furthermore, each illustration has been updated to reflect the new designs of iOS 14 and newer, and to reflect what most readers of this book see on their screens exactly. We have removed unnecessary clutter from previous illustrations that only advanced and well-versed iPhone users would have on their devices to better serve the readers. Lastly, due to reader feedback from previous editions, we have completely revamped the tips and tricks, photos, and home screen chapters to provide better information and practices. In addition, the Recommended Apps appendix has been updated to show some of the newer apps available and the list has also been retooled to apply to a broader audience, especially amid the coronavirus pandemic.

The 5th edition is the best edition yet of the *iPhone Manual for Beginners* and will have you geared up and ready to use your iPhone in just a few short hours. The average reader can finish the book in less than a day and will be surprising their friends and family when they connect to their first FaceTime call or send their first special effect photo with their Animoji! It is recommended that you keep the *iPhone Manual for Beginners* handy after you finish reading it and use the book as a reference manual as needed. We always welcome feedback on this book, and seriously take all feedback we receive into consideration when writing the new editions. To leave feedback or contact the author, please visit www.infinityguides.com or www.joemalacina.com.

Enjoy the book.

TABLE OF CONTENTS

Introduction

Congratulations! So, you have decided to take the first step, in fact the only step needed to learn how to use your iPhone. Maybe you do not even have an iPhone yet, and just want to see how it works before you decide whether to buy one. Either way, this book will teach you everything you need to know on using your device. I wanted to take this time to tell you how this book is going to be the only thing you will ever need to learn your iPhone. You see, this book was written for the perspective of a beginner. In other words, if you have never used a "smartphone" in your life, that will be no detriment when reading this book. That is the big difference between this book and other competitors available. Many authors fail to realize that even today, many people are buying their first "smartphone," and need to be shown from the ground up the basics of using and navigating their device. So that is what this book sets out to accomplish. I teach you not only how to do specific functions on your iPhone, but I will teach you the building blocks of using any "smart" device. When you are finished reading this book, not only will you be a pro using your iPhone; you will be able to pick up any smartphone or tablet and have a general understanding of how it works and how to accomplish tasks.

This book is structured so that basic concepts I teach you in beginning chapters will be used in later chapters. Therefore, I highly recommend reading the first few chapters (especially chapter 2), instead of skipping ahead to exactly what you want to learn. You may miss out on essential tidbits of information that I will not cover in detail in later chapters.

Lastly, you may be wondering if this book is suitable for you. Will it answer all the questions you have? Will you understand the material? I can assure you that the information addressed in this book is derived directly from the input of several thousand iPhone users who have had the same questions as you. I have been teaching people how to use their iPhone since 2013 and have taught well over 200,000 people of all ages and backgrounds how to use their devices. I have run a blog and numerous websites where I have received over 10,000 e-mails with questions on how to do this and how to do that. Indeed, I can assure you, I know what the most common questions are, and where the most confusion lies. Take solace in the fact that this book will address your questions with a step-by-step approach, while building your technological intuition. When you are done, you will not even need to memorize the steps to perform a function, you will have the intuition and knowledge to figure it out quickly. That is the core of what this book will teach you.

This being the 5th edition of the *iPhone Manual for Beginners*, every chapter has been updated to better explain and demonstrate the different functions of the iPhone. We have also updated every illustration and revamped the appendixes. As always, I welcome your feedback on this book and you can always reach me on Twitter @JoeMalacina or on Facebook at Facebook.com/JoeMalacina1.

On a final note, Apple users, particularly iPhone users, are notoriously loyal to their cell phones, and tend to keep using iPhones each coming year. After reading this book, you may start to see exactly why. The iPhone's interface and navigation are both seamless and soon you will find yourself liking the way it does things. Soon after that, you will notice that many other Apple devices work in very similar ways and may find yourself wanting to explore other Apple devices such as an iPad or Mac. If you ever find yourself wondering how these devices work, I urge you to check out www.infinityguides.com. There you can find beginners' books, manuals, and online courses on many Apple devices.

On that introduction, let us get started.

Chapter 1 – About the iPhone

You may now have an iPhone and you are ready to start using it. So, what is an iPhone exactly? Your iPhone is classified as a smartphone, which means that it can do everything a cell phone can do, plus additional features. With your iPhone, you can make and receive calls, browse the internet, send text messages, check your email, and use apps. You can do all this with a phone that utilizes a touch screen. Before I show you how to do all these tasks, let us familiarize ourselves with some key terms that I will use often in this book. These terms are important for you to remember, as you will encounter them often.

Key Terms

Apple ID – Let us get the trickiest one out of the way early. By far, the most common question I receive is about the Apple ID. Let me define exactly what an Apple ID is. If you have ever used an Apple device before, such as a Mac computer or iPad, you have probably encountered this term before. An Apple ID is just an email address that is associated with you and your Apple devices. You need only one Apple ID, and you can use that same Apple ID on all your Apple devices. I will go into creating an Apple ID in a chapter coming up, but for now just know that your Apple ID is your account that you will use on your iPhone. This account saves all your important data such as contacts, photos, and your purchases.

Apps – Apps are programs on your iPhone that can do tasks. Your iPhone comes with many apps already installed, and you can download many more through the App Store. Nearly every aspect within the iPhone is part of an app, which you will see later. Apps appear as square icons on your iPhone's home screen. (See Figure 1.1).

iTunes – iTunes is an app and a computer software application that is used to help you manage your iPhone's settings. There is an app on your iPhone called iTunes Store, where you can purchase and download music. More importantly, you can download iTunes software on your Windows computer, which allows you to back up your iPhone's data every time you plug it into your PC. In addition, iTunes on your computer can be used to reset your iPhone in case there is a major problem with it or if you forget your lock screen passcode. It is not necessary, and you do not need to do this now, but I highly recommend that at some point you download and install iTunes on one of your Windows computers. Instructions on how to download iTunes can be found on the website www.applevideoguides.com/itunes-install.html. If you have a Mac computer, then you do not need iTunes software.

Home Screen – Throughout this book, you will see the term home screen used often. Your home screen is the main screen of your iPhone where all your apps are shown. Every time you "Go Home", this is where you will be brought. (Figure 1.1)

Portrait & Landscape – You can view your iPhone in portrait or landscape mode. Portrait mode is the standard mode as shown in Figure 1.1. Landscape mode is when you turn your iPhone horizontal, and the contents of your iPhone become horizontally oriented. Many apps allow you to use your iPhone in landscape mode and some require it. Just know that you can change the orientation of your iPhone, and many apps allow you to do so.

[iPhones with Home Button] – In some areas of this book, you will see the **[iPhones with Home Button]** tag. This tag means that the following text is only for iPhones that have a home button. You can quickly see if your iPhone has a home button by looking at the front face near the bottom, if there is a large circular button on the front face (See <u>Figure 2.2</u>), then your iPhone has a home button. The iPhones that have home buttons that are covered in this book are: iPhone 5, iPhone 5c, iPhone 5s, iPhone 6, iPhone 6 Plus, iPhone 6s, iPhone 6s Plus, iPhone 7, iPhone 7 Plus, iPhone 8, iPhone 8 Plus, and iPhone SE. If you have an iPhone that does not have a home button, then you can skip any sections of text that have this tag.

[iPhones without Home Button] – In some areas of this book, you will see the **[iPhones without Home Button]** tag. This tag means that the following text is only for iPhones that DO NOT have a home button. The iPhones that do not have a home button are the iPhone 12, iPhone 12 Pro, iPhone 12 Pro Max, iPhone 11, iPhone 11 Pro, iPhone 11 Pro Max, iPhone XS, iPhone XS MAX, iPhone XR, and iPhone X. Any newer iPhone that does not have a home button is also included. If you have an iPhone that does have a home button, such as the iPhone SE, iPhone 8, or older iPhones, then you can skip any sections of text that have this **[iPhones without Home Button]** tag.

<u>Go Home</u> – This term will be used repeatedly throughout this book, and it simply means to go to your home screen. Going Home will be the thing you do the most on your iPhone and is very simple to accomplish. If you have an **iPhone that has a Home Button**, all you must do to <u>Go Home</u> is press the <u>home button</u>. If you have an **iPhone without a Home Button**, then all you must do to <u>Go Home</u> is perform a <u>home swipe</u> (a home swipe will be covered in Chapter 2). A home swipe accomplishes the same exact thing as pressing the home button on an iPhone with a home button. We have simply combined the two different processes into one term to make this book easier to read. So just remember, when this book instructs you to <u>Go Home</u>, press the <u>home button</u> (if you have one) on your iPhone if it is an iPhone SE or similar model; or if you have an iPhone without a home button, perform a <u>home swipe</u>.

Different iPhone Models & iOS Explained

There are many different iPhones available in the marketplace, and it is important to understand the main differences between them. Generally, most iPhones work almost entirely in the same manner. For instance, performing most tasks and functions on an iPhone 8 can be done in the exact same manner on an iPhone 12. The reason this is important is so you understand that all iPhones operate nearly exactly the same, depending upon which software they are using. So, if one friend has an iPhone 11, and your other friend has an iPhone SE, they will operate in almost the exact same way in every single aspect so long as both iPhones are using the same software version. The main differences between iPhones are where some buttons are located, such as the power button, and the hardware underneath the iPhone. Furthermore, most newer iPhones, which include the iPhone 12, 11, iPhone XS, iPhone XR, and iPhone X, do not have a *home button*, whereas every previous iPhone before the iPhone X had a *home button*. The new iPhone SE has a home button as well. All in all, remember this: No matter which iPhone you have, it will work nearly the same as every other iPhone that is running the same software. Any major differences that you might see on your iPhone will be explained thoroughly in this book.

Let us now explain the software running on iPhones. The software your iPhone is running is called its iOS. iOS stands for I Operating System, and it governs how everything in your iPhone works. iOS is labeled by a number, and the higher the number, the newer the software. For instance, the iPhone 12 and 12 Pro come with iOS 14. The iPhone 7 originally came with iOS 10. At all times you should be using the newest version of iOS available for your iPhone. I will show you how to update the iOS software in Chapter 3.5.

All of these square icons are apps.

Figure 1.1 – The Home Screen

Why Most Newer iPhone models are Different

The iPhone 12, 11, XS, XR, and X are the newest generations of iPhones to lack the signature home button. On previous iPhones and the iPhone SE, the home button is the circular button at the bottom on the front of the device. This home button was essential to using the iPhone as it would always bring you back to your home screen when pressed and performed some other useful functions. Now with most newer models the home button is no more, and has instead been replaced with the **home swipe**, which is a gesture that essentially performs what the home button still does on other iPhones. If you have used iPhones in the past, adjusting to this *home swipe* is going to take some time. This book will get you accustomed to using the *home swipe* and we will explain everything along the way; and we start now in Chapter 2.

Chapter 2 – iPhone Layout

Now we enter the "instruction manual" portion of this book, and we start with the iPhone layout. Shown in Figure 2.1 is the layout of an iPhone 12 or similar model.

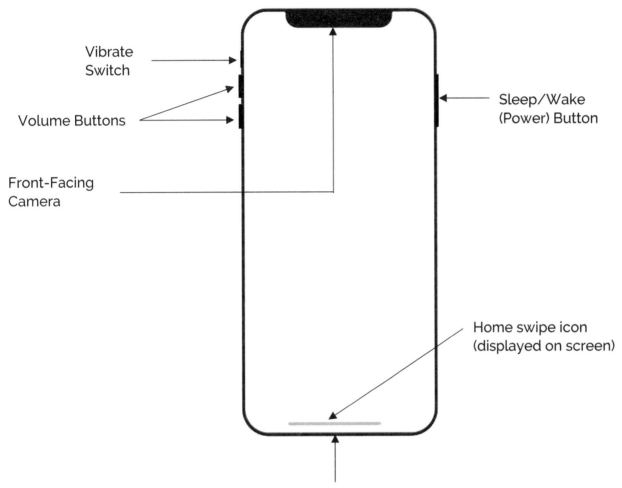

Figure 2.1 – Layout of iPhone 12 or similar model

In Figure 2.2, we have the layout of an iPhone SE or similar model. Similar models include any iPhone 8 or older iPhones. Notice that these models have a home button when compared to the 12, 11, or X-series iPhones.

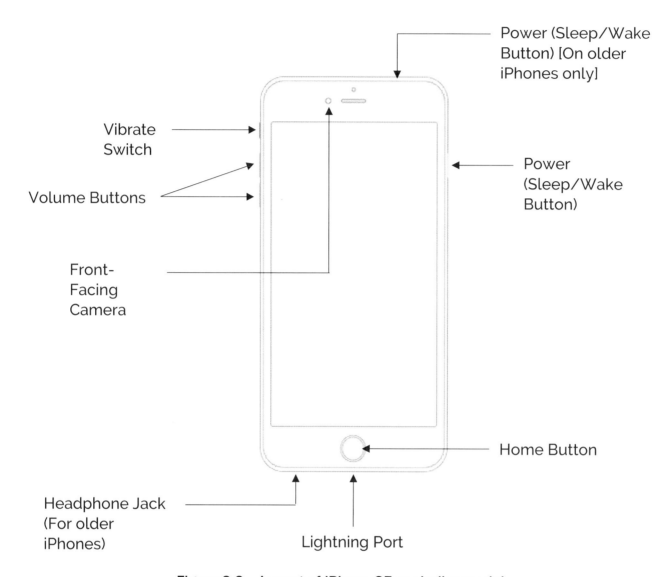

Figure 2.2 – Layout of iPhone SE or similar model

As you can see in both figures, the sleep/wake button (also known as the power button) is on the right side of the phone, while the volume buttons are on the left. On some older iPhones, the power button will be on the top side of the iPhone. Pressing the sleep/wake button turns the iPhone's screen on or off. In other words, pressing this button either puts your iPhone to sleep or wakes it up; it does not completely turn the iPhone off. The volume buttons are used to control the volume of the iPhone. Pressing the top volume button increases the volume, while pressing the bottom volume button decreases volume. Above the volume buttons is the vibrate switch. When the switch is flipped up, sound mode is enabled for the iPhone, which means your iPhone will ring when called and play sounds. When you flip the vibrate switch down, this turns on vibrate mode. In this mode, the iPhone will not ring, and will not make sounds.

At the bottom of your iPhone is the charging port. This port is called the lightning connector port, and allows you to charge your iPhone, connect accessories such as headphones, and connect your iPhone to other devices.

On the back of your iPhone is the rear camera and the flash.

[iPhones with Home Button]: If you have an iPhone SE, iPhone 8, or an older iPhone, looking at the front of the iPhone we have the most important button, the home button. The home button is the circular button on the front of the iPhone near the bottom. Pressing this button at any time will ALWAYS return you to your home screen. So, if you are inside an app and need to go to your home screen, pressing the home button will accomplish that. Also, on the front of the iPhone near the top, you can see a small circle which is the front-facing camera.

Go Home (For iPhones with Home Button Only: iPhone SE, iPhone 8 or older)

Before getting into anything else, we need to cover what is called **Go Home**. Go Home is the process of going to your home screen. If you have an iPhone SE, iPhone 8, or older iPhone, to Go Home all you need to do is press the <u>home button</u>. Each time this book instructs you to Go Home, simply press the <u>home button</u>. You can also press the <u>home button</u> to wake your iPhone's screen when it is asleep. Now if you have an iPhone without a home button, such as the iPhone 12, 12 Pro, 12 Pro Max, 11, 11 Pro, 11 Pro Max, XS, XS Max, XR or X, in order to Go Home you need to perform a <u>home swipe</u>.

Go Home (For iPhones without Home Button only)

Before getting into anything else, we need to cover what is called the *home swipe* on most newer iPhone models. On previous iPhones and the iPhone SE, there was a circular button at the bottom of the front of the device, known as the home button. Pressing this button would always bring you back to your main screen, known as the home screen. With the iPhone 12, 11, XS, XR, X, and newer iPhones, the home button has been replaced with the <u>home swipe</u>, and it is simple to perform. To perform a <u>home swipe</u>: **tap down at the bottom of your screen with your thumb or finger and swipe up and release your finger** (<u>Figure 2.3</u>).

NOTE: You do not necessarily need to swipe your finger/thumb far upwards to perform a home swipe, although you can if you want to. A ½ inch or 1 centimeter swipe from the bottom will do the trick.

To perform a home swipe, tap down at the bottom of your screen with a finger or thumb, and swipe it up the screen releasing your finger off the screen at the end. Do this quickly in one fluid motion.

TIP: When holding your iPhone in your hand, it is easiest to use your thumb to perform a home swipe. When your iPhone is placed on a surface, it is usually easiest to use a finger for a home swipe.

Figure 2.3 – How to Perform a Home Swipe [iPhones without Home Button Only]

You can do the home swipe at any time, including when your iPhone is in horizontal orientation. Practice this home swipe now as you will be performing it often. The best way to practice it is to first open any app by tapping on a square icon on your home screen (Figure 2.4.1); now perform a home swipe (Figure 2.4.2) and you should be brought back to your home screen. Try it out a couple of times to see how it works. This book will be instructing you to Go Home (perform home swipe) very often and will easily be the gesture you use the most on your iPhone, so it is prudent to become familiar with it now. Each time we instruct you to Go Home, it will be underlined in this text.

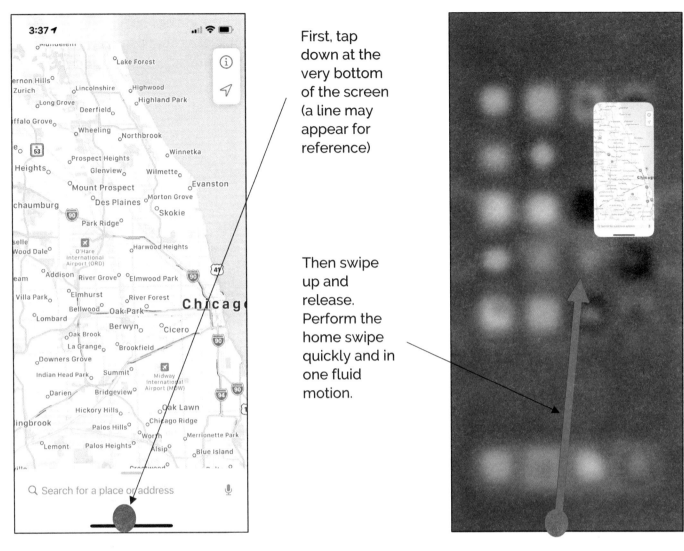

First, tap down at the very bottom of the screen (a line may appear for reference)

Then swipe up and release. Perform the home swipe quickly and in one fluid motion.

Figure 2.4.1 – Practice the Home Swipe inside an App (Maps app)

Figure 2.4.2 – The Home Swipe in Slow Motion

You can perform the home swipe at ANY TIME, and it will always bring you back to your home screen. You may need to perform the home swipe twice in order leave certain apps or when you are using your iPhone in landscape orientation.

Turning your iPhone On and Off

When your iPhone is off, you can turn it on by pressing and holding the sleep/wake button until your screen lights up. This will turn your iPhone on, and it will start booting up. After several seconds it will boot up completely.

[iPhones without Home Button]: At any time, you can turn your iPhone off by pressing and *holding* the sleep/wake button and any volume button until Figure 2.5 appears. To turn your iPhone off from this screen, place your finger down on the red power symbol, and slide it across to the right, releasing at the end. This turns your iPhone off.

[iPhones with Home Button]: At any time, you can turn your iPhone off by pressing and holding the power button until Figure 2.5 appears. To turn your iPhone off from this screen, place your finger down on the red power symbol, and slide it across to the right, releasing at the end. This turns your iPhone off.

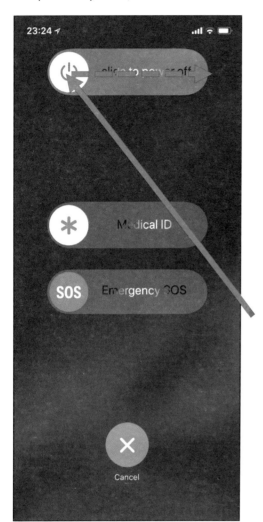

To turn iPhone off from this screen: Tap on the power icon with your finger, hold down, then swipe your finger to the right, releasing at the end.

Figure 2.5 – Shutting Down the iPhone

Waking your iPhone and Putting it to Sleep

[iPhones without Home Button]: When your iPhone is on and the screen is asleep, you can wake the screen by either pressing the sleep/wake button or by tapping on your screen. The screen will also awaken when you lift your iPhone to your face.

[iPhones with Home Button]: When your iPhone is on and the screen is asleep, you can wake the screen by pressing the home button or the power button.

Charging your iPhone

To charge your iPhone, plug the included USB cable into the bottom of your iPhone, and connect the opposite end (USB) into a USB port or charging dock. Any powered and compatible USB port will charge your iPhone including USB ports on your computer or vehicle. The charging dock can be plugged into an electrical outlet. Once your iPhone is fully charged, you should disconnect the charging cable. Newer iPhones have smart charging systems, which means the battery will charge itself optimally based on your habits. When charging your iPhone using a cable, it is recommended that you use a genuine Apple charging cable. Some iPhones use a lightning to USB-C cable, which may require an adapter to fit into ordinary USB ports. USB-C ports are smaller than regular USB.

On the iPhone 8, 8 Plus, X-series, 11, 12, and newer models, you can charge your iPhone wirelessly by using a wireless charging pad. To do this, simply place the back of your iPhone onto the charging pad, and it will begin to charge without you having to plug anything into the iPhone. Wireless charging pads are an accessory that are not included with your iPhone and can be purchased separately.

Chapter 3 – Getting Started

This chapter covers getting started with your iPhone and goes over the first-time setup procedure. If you have already completed the first-time setup where you chose your language and created your Apple ID, you can skip the first part of this chapter.

First-time Setup

When you power on your iPhone for the very first time (press and hold the <u>power button</u> when the iPhone is off), you will be brought to the first-time setup screen shown in <u>Figure 3.1</u>. This first screen will say Hello in multiple languages. Here are the steps required to move past the initial setup successfully. Please note that some of these steps may appear in a different order for you or may not appear at all. Regardless, you should be able to follow along with no issues.

1. On the Hello screen (<u>Figure 3.1</u>), tap down at the bottom of your screen and swipe up (<u>home swipe</u>) to move to the next screen or tap on the screen and swipe to the right.

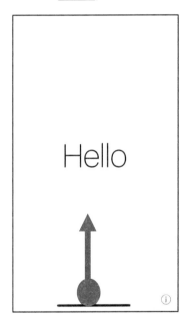

[iPhones without Home Button]: To move to the next screen, tap down on the line at the bottom of your screen with your finger, hold it there, and slide your finger upwards, and release your finger at the end. This is called a home swipe.

[iPhones with Home Button]: To move to the next screen, tap down on the screen with your finger, hold it there, and slide your finger to the right, and release your finger at the end. This is called a swipe. You may have to press the <u>home button/Go Home</u>.

Figure 3.1 – Hello Screen

2. You are now asked to select your language (<u>Figure 3.2</u>). Tap with your finger one time on the language you wish to use for your iPhone. If your language does not appear, tap down on the screen, and move your finger up or down to scroll through the list of languages. Release your finger to complete the scroll. (Swiping your finger up and down to move through a screen is called ***scrolling***, whereas tapping down on your screen with a finger and moving it in any direction and releasing is called a ***swipe***.)

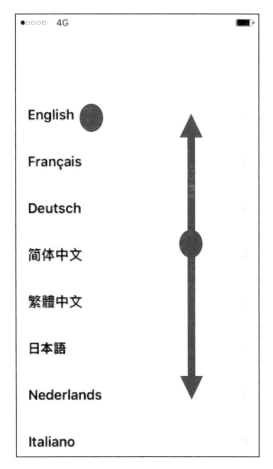

To choose your language, you can tap down on the screen with your finger and move your finger up and down the screen to "scroll" through different choices. When "scrolling", remove your finger at the end of each movement. Think of it as quickly flicking your finger up or down the screen. To choose your language, tap on the name of the language with your finger and release.

Figure 3.2 – Language

3. You will now be asked to select which country or region you live in. Select your country or region by tapping down on the correct one using your finger and release. Again, you can scroll up and down by tapping down and moving your finger up or down and releasing to move throughout the list.

4. The next screen is called the Quick Start screen and allows you to quickly set up your iPhone if you have any other iPhone or iPad around that is running iOS 11 or newer (software version). If you do have one and want to set up your iPhone this way, just turn on the other device and bring it next to your new iPhone. Doing so will set up your iPhone with the same settings and Apple ID as your other device. If not, or if you prefer to set up your iPhone manually, tap on the text at the bottom that says Set Up Manually. (In this book, we will be setting up the iPhone manually.)

5. The next screen will ask you to choose your Wi-Fi network. It is best to set up your iPhone at home so you can connect to your home wireless network. After a few moments, a list of available networks will appear on your screen. Find your home network and tap on it with your finger. A new screen will appear asking for your wireless network password. Use the keyboard that appears at the bottom of your screen to tap in the password. Simply tap each letter or number one at a time to enter it in. You can use the "back arrow" key on the keyboard to backspace, and you can use the "123" key to see numbers and symbols. Furthermore, to capitalize letters, you can use the shift key, which is the key with the upward arrow. Tapping on it will make the letters capital for ONE

entry. Once you have entered your Wi-Fi password tap <u>Join</u> on your screen, followed by tapping <u>Next</u>. (See <u>Figure 3.3</u>)

    a. If you do not have Wi-Fi available near you, or are having trouble connecting to your Wi-Fi network, you can tap on <u>Use Cellular Connection</u> at the bottom of this screen.

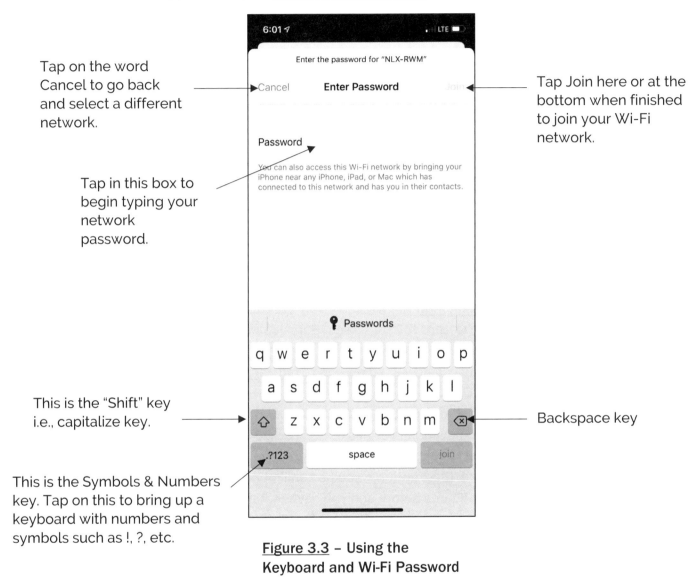

Tap on the word Cancel to go back and select a different network.

Tap Join here or at the bottom when finished to join your Wi-Fi network.

Tap in this box to begin typing your network password.

This is the "Shift" key i.e., capitalize key.

Backspace key

This is the Symbols & Numbers key. Tap on this to bring up a keyboard with numbers and symbols such as !, ?, etc.

Figure 3.3 – Using the Keyboard and Wi-Fi Password

6. Now your iPhone will attempt to activate itself. This can take a few minutes. Once this is completed you will be brought to a new screen to set up Face or Touch ID, or a screen educating you about Data & Privacy.

7. Tap <u>Continue</u> at the bottom of the Data & Privacy screen to continue.

    a. **[iPhones without Home Button]:** Now you will be prompted to set up Face ID. Face ID allows you to unlock your iPhone just by looking at it. I recommend setting this up now. Tap on <u>Continue</u>.

        i. Tap <u>Get Started</u> and follow the instructions on your screen to set up Face ID. You will be asked to hold your iPhone up and look directly at the screen, bringing your face into position inside the circle. Once your face is positioned, hold your iPhone steady and move your head around in a complete circle.

    ii.   Once the first scan is complete, tap Continue.

    iii.   Complete the circular motion again.

    iv.   Once the second scan is complete, your iPhone will show "Face ID is now set up." Tap Continue.

  b. **[iPhones with Home Button]:** Now you will be asked to set up Touch ID if your iPhone is capable of it. For now, tap on Set up Touch ID later.

8. Next, you will be asked to set up a passcode. A passcode is a 6-digit PIN that allows you to unlock your iPhone. You will need to remember this PIN, so I recommend writing it down somewhere safe. You will have to enter this PIN each time you restart your iPhone, and each time Face ID/Touch ID fails to work properly. I CANNOT STRESS ENOUGH THAT YOU SHOULD WRITE DOWN AND REMEMBER THE PASSCODE YOU CREATE. IF YOU FORGET YOUR PASSCODE, THE PROCESS OF GETTING BACK INTO YOUR IPHONE IS DIFFICULT AND TIME CONSUMING. Once you have decided on a passcode, enter it in your iPhone by tapping on the numbers. Once you have entered it the first time, you will be asked to confirm the passcode you created by entering it again. Do so and you will be brought to the next screen.

  a. If you prefer, you can use a 4-digit code or alphabetic code instead of a 6-digit passcode. To do this, tap on Passcode options. I will show you later how to change your passcode.

9. Next you will be brought to the Apps & Data screen. Here you must choose how to set up your iPhone.

  a. If this is your first iPhone, you will tap on Don't Transfer Apps & Data or set up as new iPhone. (**Most Likely Option**)

  b. If you have owned an iPhone before, and you want to migrate all your previous data to this new iPhone, and you know that previous data is backed up on iCloud, which is Apple's backup service, tap on Restore from iCloud Backup. You will then be asked to enter your Apple ID and password. (Best option if you had an iPhone previously.)

  c. If you have owned an iPhone before and you have that iPhone's data saved on your Mac or on a Windows PC with iTunes, tap on Restore from Mac or PC or Restore from iTunes Backup. You will then be told to plug your iPhone into your computer that has the backup installed.

  d. If you previously had an iPhone and still have physical possession of it, you can transfer your previous iPhone's data to your new one by tapping on Transfer Directly from iPhone. You will then need to use your previous iPhone to transfer the data.

  e. Lastly, if your previous phone was an Android phone and you want to migrate that data over, tap on Move Data from Android and follow the instructions on the screen. This option is a little more complicated and not recommended for new users.

10. Next, you will be brought to the Apple ID screen. THIS SCREEN AND THIS STEP IS VERY IMPORTANT. PLEASE FOLLOW THIS STEP VERY CAREFULLY. On this screen you are asked to log in with your Apple ID. If you have ever owned an iPhone or iPad, chances are you have an Apple ID. Furthermore, if you currently use a Mac computer, you may already have an Apple ID as well. This next sentence is

very important. If you have other Apple devices and have an Apple ID, it is very important that you use the same Apple ID for all your Apple devices. This way, all your purchases on one Apple ID will be available on all your devices. Just to reiterate from earlier, an Apple ID is an email address you have associated with an Apple device. If you know you already have an Apple ID, go to step 10A. If you do not have an Apple ID or are unsure, go to step 10B.

a. If you already have an Apple ID from previous Apple devices, tap into the box to the right of the text "Apple ID" and enter your Apple ID email address. Remember, this is your email address that you have registered as an Apple ID with Apple. After you enter your email address, tap <u>Next</u> or <u>return</u> on your keyboard and then type in your Apple ID password. When you are done, tap <u>Next</u> at the upper right.

b. If you do not have an Apple ID, or this is your first Apple device, or you are not sure if you have an Apple ID, tap on the text at the bottom that says, "<u>Don't have an Apple ID or forgot it?</u>"

    i. On the next screen you can tap on "<u>Forgot Apple ID or Password</u>" if you think you have an Apple ID from a previous Apple device. If you do not have an Apple ID, tap on <u>Create a Free Apple ID</u>. **PLEASE NOTE, SETTING UP AN APPLE ID IS HIGHLY RECOMMENDED AS YOU NEED AN APPLE ID TO DOWNLOAD APPS, BACKUP YOUR DEVICE, AND USE OTHER CRITICAL FEATURES.

        1. To create an Apple ID, you will be asked to enter in some information about yourself. This information is needed to create your account. The type of information that may be requested includes: your name, email address, phone number, date of birth, credit card information, and secret questions.

        2. Follow the instructions on your screen to create your Apple ID.

        3. At some point you will be asked which email address you want to use as your Apple ID. You can either use an email address you already have or create a new iCloud email address. I suggest using a personal email address you already have that you check often.

        4. After inputting your email address that you want to use for your Apple ID, you will be required to create a password for your Apple ID. This password is NOT the same as your email address password. Instead, you must create a password for your new Apple ID. The password must contain at least 8 characters, and it must contain at least 1 capital letter, 1 lower case letter, and at least 1 number.

            a. Now tap into the verify box and type in your new password again to verify it is the same. REMEMBER THIS PASSWORD. WRITE IT DOWN SOMEWHERE SAFE IF YOU MUST, BUT YOU WILL NEED THIS PASSWORD LATER. When done, tap <u>Next</u> at the upper right.

        5. You also may be asked to verify your identity using a phone number or some other contact method. The phone number of your iPhone should automatically fill this box, so just tap on <u>Next</u> at the upper right here. If your

phone number does not fill in automatically, enter a phone number you can be contacted at.

6. Once you have completed all the steps, your Apple ID will be created. This can take a few minutes, and once it is complete you may be brought to a screen that will prompt you to set up your email address that you used for your Apple ID on your iPhone. This step is completely optional. Tap <u>Next</u> at the upper right.

11. The creation or login of your Apple ID is over. Now you will be brought to a Terms and Conditions page. Once you have reviewed the information on the page and you agree to it, tap on <u>Agree</u>. It may take a minute or two for your iPhone to finish setting up your Apple ID.

12. Now you will be brought to an Express Settings page. Tap on <u>Continue</u> at the bottom to proceed. You also may be brought to the Location Services page; which I recommend you choose to <u>Enable</u> so your iPhone can use your location.

13. The next screen will ask you if you want to automatically keep your iPhone's software up to date. I recommend tapping on <u>Continue</u> here.

14. On the next screen, you may be asked to set up Apple Pay. Apple Pay lets you pay for items and services using your iPhone and is accepted at many terminals. You can choose to set up Apple Pay now by tapping on Continue or you can set it up later by tapping on <u>Set Up Later in Wallet</u>. To set up Apple Pay, you will need a credit card handy.

15. The next screen will be the Siri screen. On this screen you will be asked whether you want to set up Siri. I recommend you set it up now, so tap on <u>Continue</u>. Follow the directions that appear on your screen. You may be asked to speak a few phrases to your iPhone. All this does is train Siri to recognize your voice. Siri is Apple's artificial helper, which listens to you and follows your commands. Once this step is complete, your iPhone will read "Hey Siri is Ready," and you can tap on <u>Continue</u>. If you are having trouble setting up Siri, just tap on <u>Set Up Later in Settings</u> at the bottom of your screen.

16. The next few screens will explain some features of the iPhone to you and show you some options, such as Screen Time, App Analytics, True Tone Display, Appearance, Go Home (on iPhones without Home Button), Dock, Recent Apps, and the Control Center. You can read through these screens, select any options you wish, and tap on <u>Continue</u> on each screen to move through them.

17. You are all done! You should see the "Welcome to iPhone" screen. Tap on <u>Get Started</u> or <u>Go Home</u> to proceed and to access your home screen. (Remember, Go Home is an important term you will need to remember. Revisit Chapter 2 if you do not know what it means.)

After you have completed the initial setup you will be brought to your home screen. Remember, your home screen is the screen that shows all your apps.

Chapter 3.5 – Update your iOS Now

Before we begin Chapter 4, it is important that you check to see if an update is available to your iPhone's software, otherwise known as iOS. To do this, follow these steps:

1. On your home screen, which shows all your apps, there should be an app called Settings. Tap on the app with your finger to open it. (Figure 3.5.1)

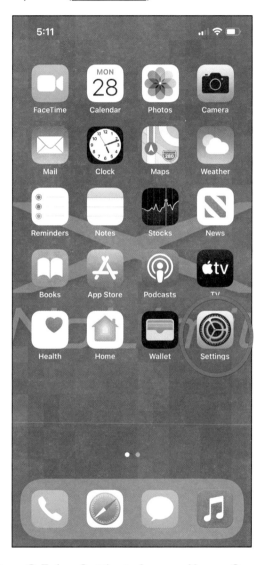

Figure 3.5.1 – Settings App on Home Screen

2. Next, tap on the word General, which you should see somewhere on your screen. You can scroll up and down if you cannot find it. (Figure 3.5.2)

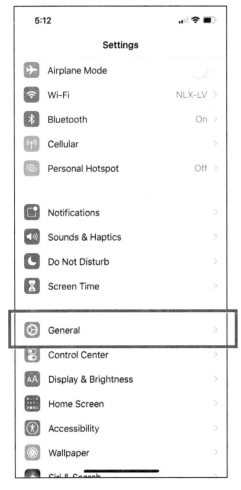

Figure 3.5.2 – Settings -> General

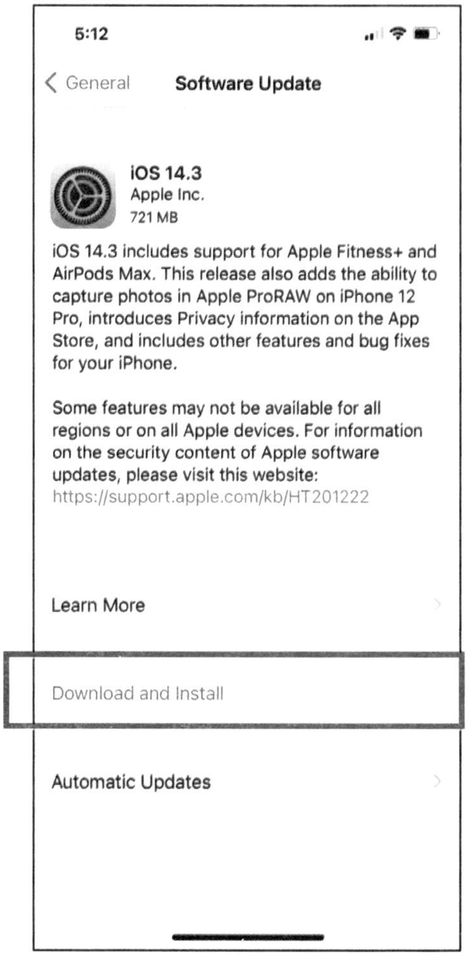

Figure 3.5.3 – Settings -> General -> Software Update

3. Next, tap on Software Update. (Figure 3.5.3)
4. Your iPhone will check to see if there is an update available. If there is an update available, your iPhone will say so, and there will be an option to Download and Install. If this option appears, tap on Download and Install or Install. If there is not an update available, your iPhone will say iOS X.y.z, where the X, y, and z will be numbers. For the sake of this book, the only number that matters is the first number. So, for this book, you will want that first number to be 14 or greater if you have an iPhone 6s, 7, 8, X, XR, XS, 11, 12, or SE. If you have an iPhone 6, 5s, 5, or 5c, then you will want that first number to be 10 or greater. It will also say your Software is Up to Date.
5. If an update is available, install the update by tapping on Install or Download and Install. Your iPhone will download and install the software update. This could take some time, and you will need to be connected to Wi-Fi to download the update. (See Chapter 4 to learn how to connect to Wi-Fi if you did not do so in the initial setup). Let the update install, and your iPhone will restart when it is finished, and then you are ready to continue. If your iOS software is already up to date, then you are ready to continue.
6. You can Go Home on your iPhone to return to the home screen.

If a software update is available for your iPhone, it is HIGHLY recommended that you update it.

Chapter 4 – Navigating your iPhone

All you need to use your iPhone are your fingers. Everything is based on the touch screen and the Go Home feature. Here at the home screen (Figure 4.1), which is just the screen that shows you all your apps, you can open an app, which is a program on your phone that can do tasks and enable features, by lightly touching down on the square with your finger and releasing quickly. To then leave the app and return to the home screen, Go Home (See Chapter 2 if you forgot what Go Home means).

Your home screen is made up of multiple screens to accommodate however many apps and widgets you have on your iPhone. To move through different pages of apps on your iPhone's home screen, touch down on the screen with one of your fingers, and then drag your finger to the left or the right, like you would be dragging a page, then release. If at any time you need to return to the main home screen, just Go Home.

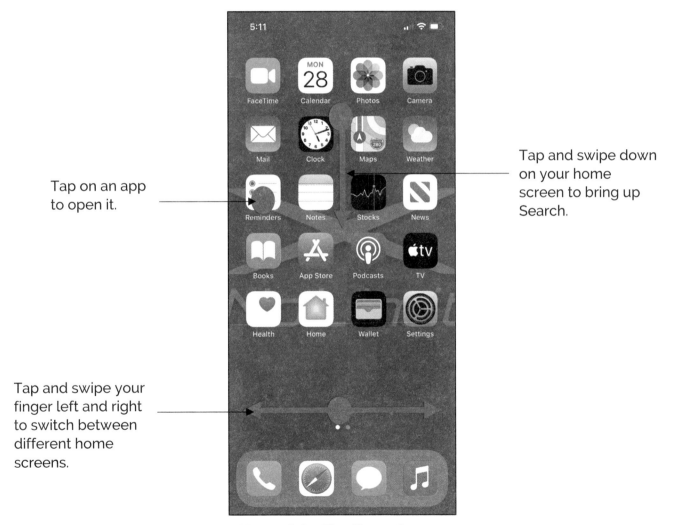

Tap on an app to open it.

Tap and swipe down on your home screen to bring up Search.

Tap and swipe your finger left and right to switch between different home screens.

Figure 4.1 – The Home Screen

Search your iPhone

You can search your iPhone for anything using the Search function. To use this function, touch down near the middle of your home screen and drag your finger down then release (Figure 4.1). This is a great way to search for apps on your iPhone when you have too many to remember them all. To get back to the home screen simply Go Home or swipe up with your finger.

Today View

You may have noticed that when you are on your main home screen and you swipe your finger to the right that you are brought to what is called the "Today View" (Figure 4.2). This screen shows you if you have anything coming up on your calendar, along with some suggestions for apps that you use. There may also be additional information on this screen such as your local weather and news. You can tap on anything here to explore it more. To get back to the home screen, Go Home or swipe your finger to the left.

Figure 4.2 – The Today View

Connecting to Wi-Fi

Connecting to Wi-Fi is one of the most important things you should do with your iPhone. When you are connected to Wi-Fi, your internet speeds are generally faster, and you are not using valuable cellular data. You may have connected to your home wireless network when you first set up your iPhone, in which case you are already good to go. You can tell if you are connected to Wi-Fi by looking for the Wi-Fi symbol at the top right of your screen. If the Wi-Fi symbol appears, it means you are connected to Wi-Fi (Figure 4.3). Once you have connected to a Wi-Fi network, your iPhone will remember that network, and you will not need to ever connect manually to it again. Each time your iPhone comes in range of that network it will connect automatically.

To connect to a Wi-Fi network, follow these steps:

1. Open the Settings app on your home screen by tapping down on it and quickly releasing.
2. Tap Wi-Fi.
3. Your iPhone will search for networks. If you are already connected to a network, it will appear directly under the words Wi-Fi and a checkmark will be next to its name. Look at the network names under where it says "NETWORKS". When you see the network you want to connect to, tap on it with your finger.
4. You will then have to enter your Wi-Fi password. Enter this password using the keyboard, and then tap on Join at the upper right. (For more on using the iPhone keyboard, see Figure 3.3 in Chapter 3).
5. Your iPhone will join the Wi-Fi network if the password was entered correctly. Remember, Wi-Fi passwords are case sensitive. Once you have joined a Wi-Fi network, you will never have to manually join that network again, as your iPhone will connect to it automatically from now on.
6. Go Home to return to the home screen.

TIP: If you do not know your home wireless network name and password, it may be located on the back or bottom of your wireless router. Check the back of your router to see if that information is there.

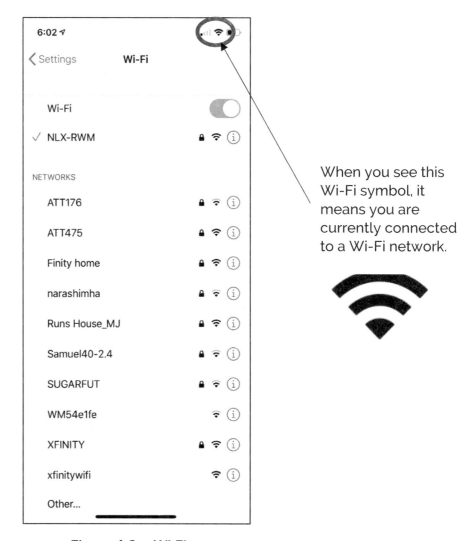

When you see this Wi-Fi symbol, it means you are currently connected to a Wi-Fi network.

Figure 4.3 – Wi-Fi

Chapter 5 – Apple ID

I have already discussed the concept of your Apple ID several times throughout this text, but it is worth emphasizing some more. The most common questions I receive about using iPhones are related to Apple IDs. In this chapter, I will cover everything you need to know about your Apple ID.

How to Check Your Apple ID

If you created an Apple ID during the initial setup of your iPhone, great! If you did, please write down your Apple ID email and password somewhere safe. You will need that information from time to time. If you have not created an Apple ID or are not sure, there is a way to check. Follow these steps:

1. Open the Settings app on your iPhone by tapping on Settings on your home screen.
2. Tap the big box at the top of your screen that should have your name inside it. (See Figure 5.2)
3. On this screen, at the top, will be your name with an email address below it. This email address is your Apple ID if you created one and are signed in. If there is not an email address in there, it will read "Sign In" instead. (See Figure 5.1)

Now you know whether you are signed into your iPhone with an Apple ID, and what that Apple ID is. If you are signed in, write down and remember your Apple ID. If you are not signed in, and do not have an Apple ID, you need to create one now.

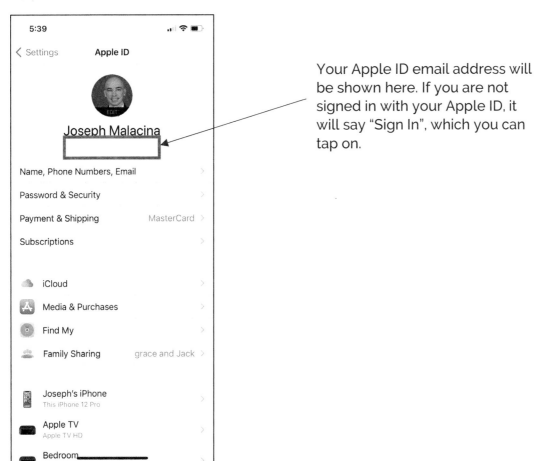

Your Apple ID email address will be shown here. If you are not signed in with your Apple ID, it will say "Sign In", which you can tap on.

Figure 5.1 – Settings -> Big Box at Top with your Name

How to Create an Apple ID

If you do not have an Apple ID, you need to create one. Simply put, you need an Apple ID to use many of the functions available on your iPhone. To create an Apple ID, follow these steps:

1. Go to your home screen. (Remember, you can get to your home screen at any time by performing the Go Home action. If you forgot how to Go Home, see Chapter 2.)

2. Find the app called iTunes Store and tap on it to open it.
3. When the app loads completely, scroll down to the very bottom and tap Sign In.
4. If you have an Apple ID, sign in with your Apple ID login credentials by tapping on Use Existing Apple ID. If you do not have one, tap on Create New Apple ID.
5. On the next screen, enter an existing email address that you use regularly. This email address will become your Apple ID.
6. Next you will have to create a password for your Apple ID. This is not the same as your email address's password; it is a separate password for your Apple ID. Type in a password and type it in again in the Verify box. Passwords must contain at least 8 characters, and must contain at least one number, one capitalized letter, and one lowercase letter.
7. Choose your region if it is not automatically filled in for you and agree to the terms and conditions (if applicable) by reading them and tapping on the tab next to them.
8. When done, tap Next at the upper right.
9. At the next screen you will have to fill in your personal information and select security questions for your account. The security questions are for in case you forget your password. Fill everything in, along with the security questions and answers, and tap Next when done.
10. Next you will have to enter billing information. You will not be charged anything, but this billing information is required in case you decide to purchase anything in the future and to verify your identity. Fill out the form and then tap Next at the upper right.
11. There are a few more steps left that are self-explanatory. Follow the instructions on your screen to complete the creation of your Apple ID. You may be asked to verify your phone number and/or your email address.
12. When all the steps have completed, your Apple ID will have been successfully created. Occasionally, you may be asked for your Apple ID password on your iPhone. When you are asked, enter it in on your keyboard. Remember to use correct capitalization.

*Alternatively, you can create an Apple ID from a computer by visiting https://appleid.apple.com/account (Recommended if creating an Apple ID on your iPhone becomes too tedious or confusing).

Signing in with Your Apple ID

If you have created your Apple ID on your iPhone, you will most likely be signed in automatically on your iPhone. Your Apple ID is used for many apps and services, and it may be necessary to sign in to all of these Apple services with your Apple ID. Once signed in, you will not need to ever do this again. Follow these steps to sign in to your iPhone with your Apple ID:

1. On your home screen open the Settings app.

2. Tap <u>on the big box at the very top where it says Apple ID or your name</u> (<u>Figure 5.2</u>).

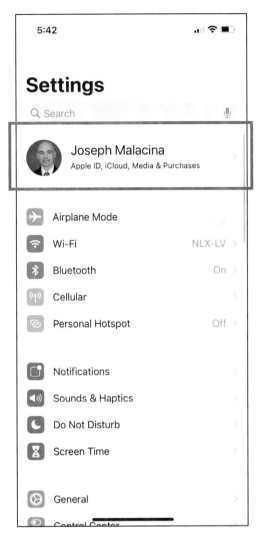

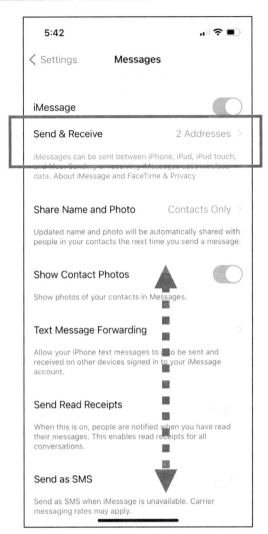

Figure 5.2 – Settings -> Big Box at Top (Apple ID)

Figure 5.3 – Settings -> Messages -> Send & Receive

3. At the top will be your name and email address if you are already signed into your Apple ID for iCloud. If your name does not appear, tap on <u>Sign In</u>.
4. Enter your Apple ID email address and password and tap <u>Sign In</u>.
5. Use the <u>back arrows</u> again at the upper left to return to the main Settings page.
6. Now we want to check and make sure your Apple ID is signed in for all Apple services.
7. Find in Settings the <u>Messages</u> box and tap it.
8. First, make sure <u>iMessage</u> is enabled. (The selector will be colored green if it is.)
9. Now tap where it says <u>Send & Receive</u>. (<u>Figure 5.3</u>)
10. At the top where it says YOU CAN RECEIVE IMESSAGES TO AND REPLY FROM, make sure both your Apple ID and phone number are checked. If one is not checked, tap it to checkmark it.
11. For the area that states START NEW CONVERSATIONS FROM, I recommend that you only have your

     phone number checked here.

12. Use the <u>back arrows</u> at the upper left to return to the main Settings page and then tap on <u>FaceTime</u>.
13. In the YOU CAN BE REACHED BY FACETIME AT box, make sure both your phone number and Apple ID are check marked. If one is not check marked, tap on it.
14. Perform the <u>Go Home</u> action to return to the home screen.

You should now be signed in completely with your Apple ID.

How to Use Your Apple ID

Now that you are all signed in with your Apple ID, how can you use it? You do not really need to worry about that. You will be using your Apple ID automatically. Every time you download an app you will be using your Apple ID. Occasionally, your iPhone may show a popup box asking you for your Apple ID password. When this appears, just enter your password, and tap <u>OK/Sign In</u>. Your iPhone will ask for your Apple ID password periodically for security purposes. Make sure you remember this password!

All the confusing stuff is now out of the way. Once you are signed in with your Apple ID, you do not need to worry about it anymore if you remember your Apple ID password. It is finally time to get into using the iPhone.

Chapter 6 – Your Contact List

Your contact list is an essential tool on your iPhone. With it, you can store your contacts' phone numbers, email addresses, and other vital data.

Importing Contacts

When you first get your new iPhone, there will be no contacts in your contact list. If you previously had an iPhone or other Apple device, then you can automatically transfer those existing contacts into your iPhone. All you need to do to accomplish this is make sure you sign in with the same Apple ID on both devices. Once you are signed in with the same Apple ID on both devices, your devices will share these contacts and they will automatically populate.

There are other ways of transferring your contacts into your iPhone. Some wireless provider stores can do this automatically using their own equipment. If you want to transfer your contacts from an older non-Apple phone to your new iPhone, then you should contact your wireless provider's store and see if they can do that for you. Unfortunately, for some cell phones you will not be able to do this, in which case you will have to create your contacts manually.

You can also import your Outlook contacts to your iPhone using iTunes software on a Windows PC. This is much more complicated and can be learned by visiting www.infinityguides.com and searching for "iTunes".

Creating Contacts

Let us see how we can create a contact. Here are the steps: (See Figures 6.1 & 6.2)

1. Open the Phone app from your home screen.
2. At the bottom, tap on the tab that says Contacts. (Figure 6.1)

Figure 6.1 – Phone App -> Contacts Tab

3. At the upper right of your screen, there will be a + sign. Tap on the + sign. (Figure 6.1)
4. You will now be brought to a screen where you can create a contact.
5. Tap into each corresponding box to type in an entry for the new contact. You can enter in their First name, Last name, and Company.
6. Tap into the add phone box to add their phone number.
7. Tap into the add email box to add their email, if applicable.
8. By scrolling down further, you can choose to enter in additional information including their home address, birthday, and other information.
9. You can also choose a specific ringtone for a contact.
10. Once you have added all the information you want for your new contact, tap Done at the upper right.
11. Your new contact has just been created.

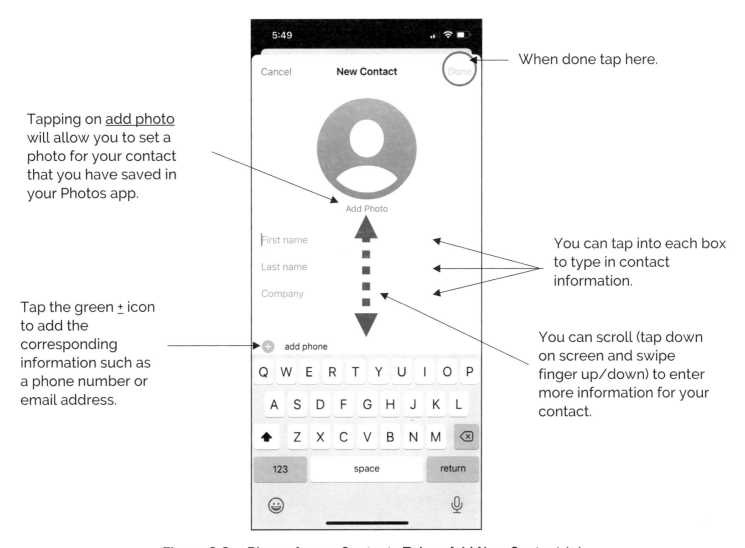

Tapping on <u>add photo</u> will allow you to set a photo for your contact that you have saved in your Photos app.

When done tap here.

You can tap into each box to type in contact information.

Tap the green <u>+</u> icon to add the corresponding information such as a phone number or email address.

You can scroll (tap down on screen and swipe finger up/down) to enter more information for your contact.

<u>Figure 6.2</u> – Phone App -> Contacts Tab -> Add New Contact (+)

Browsing Contacts

At any time, you can view your contact list by opening the <u>Phone</u> app and tapping the <u>Contacts</u> tab at the bottom. Now you will see a list of all your contacts (<u>Figure 6.1</u>). You can browse through this list by simply tapping down on the <u>screen</u> and scrolling (swiping) up or down.

TIP: To quickly browse through your contacts by their last name. Tap down and scroll on the <u>letters</u> at the far right of your screen.

You can also tap into the <u>Search bar</u> at the top of your Contacts screen to search for a contact directly.

To view a contact's information, simply tap on their *name*.

Editing or Deleting a Contact

To edit a contact, tap on their *name* inside the contact list, and then tap <u>edit</u> at the upper right. Now you can edit all their information. To delete a certain aspect of their information, simply tap on the <u>red minus sign</u> next to it. When you are done editing a contact, tap on <u>Done</u> at the upper right.

To delete a contact, tap on their _name_ inside the contact list. Now tap edit at the upper right. Now scroll down all the way to the bottom of the contact's information and tap on Delete Contact. A confirmation will appear, where you can tap on Delete Contact again to confirm the deletion.

Favorites List

The Favorites List is basically the speed dial of your iPhone. To access you Favorites List, open the Phone app, and then tap the Favorites tab. To add a contact to your Favorites List, first tap the plus sign at the upper left-hand corner. Then scroll to the contact you wish to add to your favorites, and then tap on that contact. Now tap on which segment of that contact you want to be on your favorites list, such as text message or phone call. Your contact will now appear in your favorites list. (Figure 6.3)

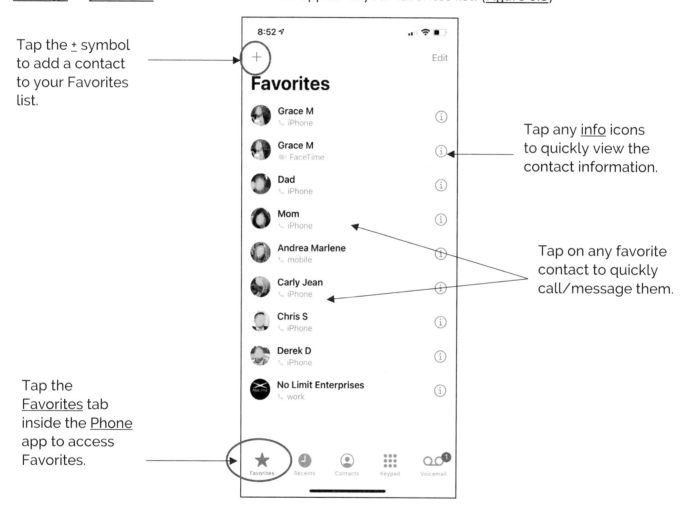

Tap the ± symbol to add a contact to your Favorites list.

Tap any info icons to quickly view the contact information.

Tap on any favorite contact to quickly call/message them.

Tap the Favorites tab inside the Phone app to access Favorites.

Figure 6.3 – Phone App -> Favorites Tab

Chapter 7 – Phone Calls

At its heart, the iPhone is a great cell phone. Making and receiving calls is easy and user-friendly, and we will explore that in this chapter.

Making a Call

There are numerous ways to make a call using your iPhone. I will cover some of the most basic ways.

How to Dial a Call (Figure 7.1)

1. Open the Phone app on your home screen.
2. Tap the Keypad tab at the bottom.
3. Tap in the number you wish to call, one digit at a time.
4. Tap the green phone icon to start the call.

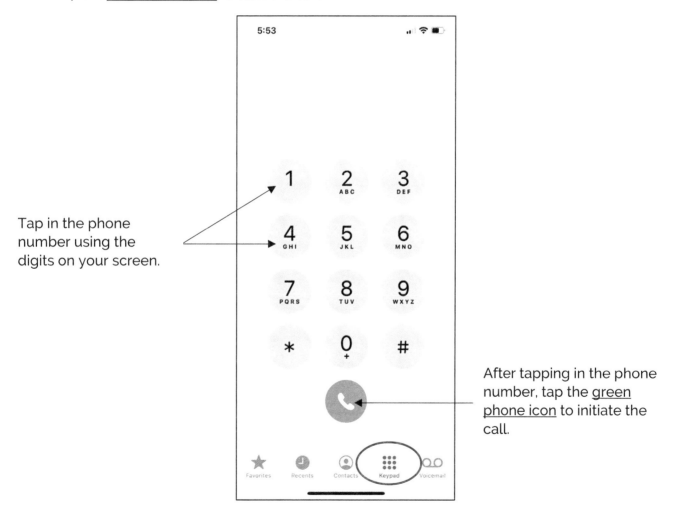

Tap in the phone number using the digits on your screen.

After tapping in the phone number, tap the green phone icon to initiate the call.

Figure 7.1 – Phone App -> Keypad Tab

How to Call Someone on Your Contact List (Figure 7.2)

1. Open the Phone app.
2. Tap the Contacts tab.
3. Find the contact you wish to call and tap on their *name* to view their contact details.
4. Now, to start the call you can either tap the call icon inside the contact's information or tap on the corresponding phone number within the contact to start the call.

Tap on any of the blue icons to initiate the action (i.e., a phone call, text message, email, etc.)

You can also tap directly on their contact information to start a call, email, or text message.

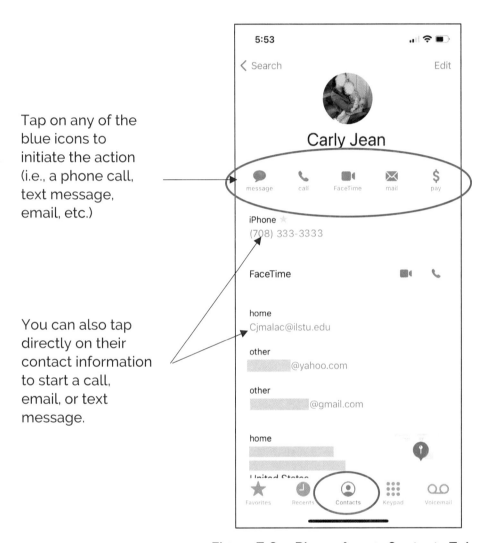

Figure 7.2 – Phone App -> Contacts Tab

How to Call Someone on Your Favorites List (See Figure 6.3)

1. Open the Phone app.
2. Tap the Favorites tab.
3. Tap on the *contact* in your Favorites List that has a small phone icon underneath their name to immediately start a call with them.

Receiving a Call

When you receive a call while your iPhone's screen is unlocked (i.e., you are currently using your iPhone), a notification will appear the top of your screen (Figure 7.3). To answer the call, tap on the green phone icon. To reject the call, tap on the red phone icon. You can bring up additional options by tapping on the notification and swiping it down the screen (See Figure 7.3). You can ignore the call by tapping on the notification and swiping it up and off the screen. All you need to do to answer the call is tap on the green phone icon. When you do so, you will now be connected to the call.

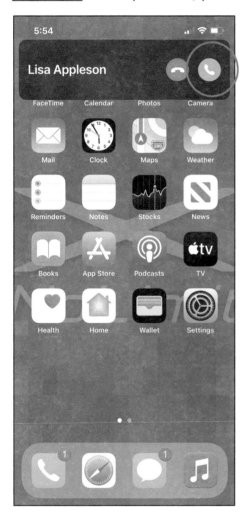

Figure 7.3 – Receiving a Call, iPhone Unlocked

When you receive a call when your iPhone is currently locked, you will see a slider at the bottom of your screen (Figure 7.4). To answer the call, touch down on the green phone icon, and slide it to the right with your finger, releasing at the end. This will connect you to the call.

To answer the call, tap down on the <u>green phone icon</u> and slide your finger to the right, releasing at the end.

Figure 7.4 – Receiving a Call, iPhone Locked

You can always reject a call by pressing the <u>sleep/wake button</u> on your iPhone when a call is incoming. Press it once to silence the incoming call and press it again to reject the call.

Call Functions

During a phone call, you have several functions available to you. Looking at your screen during a call (<u>Figure 7.5</u>), there are several icons on your screen. They do the following if you tap on them:

- **Mute –** Mutes your side of the call. In other words, the person you are talking to on the phone will not be able to hear anything from your side until you touch <u>mute</u> again to turn mute off.
- **Keypad –** Brings up a touch-tone keypad in case you need to work through a touch-tone system.
- **Speaker/Audio –** Tapping <u>speaker</u> or <u>audio</u> turns on speakerphone. Tap it again to turn it off. You can also use this button to change the call audio output, such as to a Bluetooth device.
- **Add Call –** Tapping on <u>add call</u> lets you add another person to the call, such as 3-way calling (If part of your service).

- **FaceTime –** FaceTime lets you connect to the person you are talking to over a FaceTime call, which is a video call. This only works when you are talking to someone who has a FaceTime enabled device (more on FaceTime later in this book).
- **Contacts –** Tapping on contacts will bring you to your contact list.

You can also browse through your iPhone while on a call by performing the Go Home action. To get back to the call screen itself mid-call, tap on the time with a green highlight around it at the top left of your screen **[iPhones without Home Button]** or by tapping the green bar at the top of your screen **[iPhones with Home Button]**.

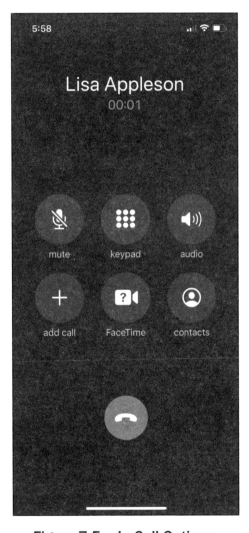

Figure 7.5 – In-Call Options

Recent Calls

To access your recent calls list, open the Phone app and touch the Recents tab at the bottom. This screen lists all your recent calls. For names listed in red, these are missed calls. The times indicated on the right are the times the call took place. To quickly call someone on your recent calls list, simply tap down on their *name* and your iPhone will call them. You can also view more information about a recent call by tapping on the information circle to the right.

Voicemail

(See Figure 7.6)

A common question I get is how to set up voicemail on the iPhone. Unfortunately, there is no easy answer. The reason is because voicemail is completely controlled by your cellular provider. You will have to contact them to set it up.

For some providers, you can set up voicemail from the Phone app. Just open the Phone app, tap on the Voicemail tab at the bottom right, and your voicemails will be listed. You can tap on one to listen to it. You can also set your voicemail greeting by tapping on Greeting at the upper left. Again, this setup will not work for everyone, as it is completely controlled by your cellular provider. Your best bet is to contact them to set your voicemail up.

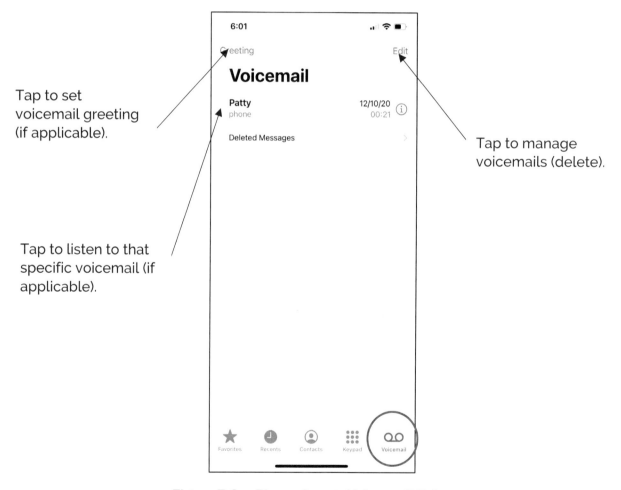

Figure 7.6 – Phone App -> Voicemail Tab

Chapter 8 – Text Messaging

The iPhone is a wonderful tool for text messaging. The ease in which to send and receive text messages is astounding, and the way in which texts are organized is even better. Let us explore the Messages app.

Somewhere on your home screen will be the Messages app. Tap on it to open it up. This is where all your text messaging will take place, and where all your text messages will be stored.

Before we dive in, let me explain some texting jargon. When you exchange a text message with someone, it is generally called a conversation or thread. In this book, we will call any text conversation with someone or a group of people a "thread". (Figure 8.1)

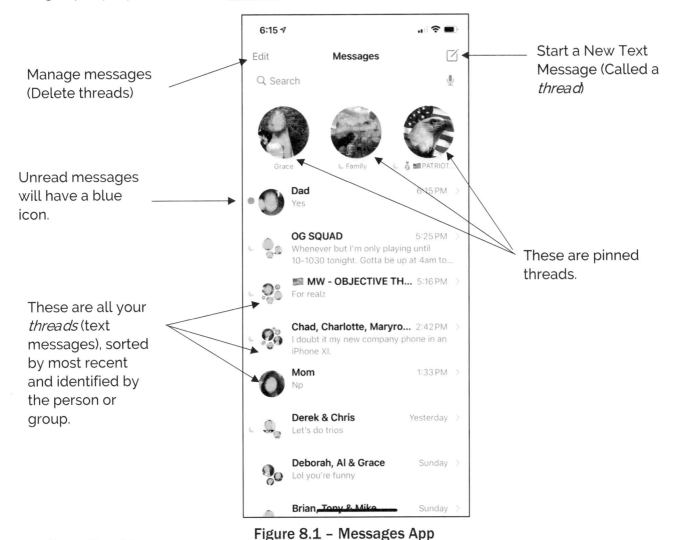

Manage messages
(Delete threads)

Start a New Text
Message (Called a
thread)

Unread messages
will have a blue
icon.

These are pinned
threads.

These are all your
threads (text
messages), sorted
by most recent
and identified by
the person or
group.

Figure 8.1 – Messages App

Sending a Text Message

To send your first text message on your iPhone, first tap the Square and Pencil icon at the upper right of your screen inside the Messages app (Figure 8.1). This will start a new text thread. In the screen that appears, you can type in the name of one your contacts and as you are typing, your iPhone will make suggestions as to whom you are trying to text. Once you see their name, you can tap on their *name* to complete the entry. (Figure 8.2)

Alternatively, you can use your keyboard to type in the exact phone number of someone you want to text.

Next you can tap into the Message bar or iMessage bar near the middle of your screen. Now you can use your keypad to type in a message. Once that message is ready to be sent, tap the blue or green up arrow icon to send the message. (Figure 8.2)

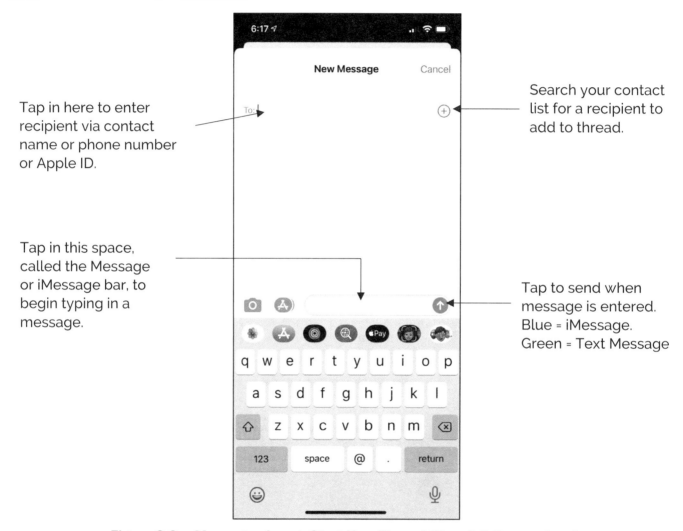

Tap in here to enter recipient via contact name or phone number or Apple ID.

Search your contact list for a recipient to add to thread.

Tap in this space, called the Message or iMessage bar, to begin typing in a message.

Tap to send when message is entered. Blue = iMessage. Green = Text Message

Figure 8.2 – Messages App -> Start New Thread (Pencil & Square Icon)

Receiving a Message

When you receive a message, it will appear in the Messages app (See Figure 8.1). Unread messages will have a blue icon next to the thread. To view the message, open the thread by tapping on the thread's *name*. Your entire text message conversation will now be shown, including any new messages that you have received from this thread. You can scroll up and down through the history of the conversation using your finger. At any time while inside a thread, you can return to the main Messages screen by tapping on the back arrow at the upper left.

Group Threads

Text messaging is not reserved for a single person. You can create group threads where multiple people can exchange text messages. The process is the same:

1. Tap the <u>square and pencil icon</u> at the upper right to create a new message.
2. Enter in the name of a person you want to text of the group. Tap on their _name_ once it appears in suggestions.
3. Now type in another name of a person you also want to be a part of the group thread and tap on their _name_ in suggestions when it appears.
4. Add as many people to the thread as you wish.
5. When ready to start conversing, tap into the <u>Message box</u> and begin typing away.

This group thread will now be saved in your Messages app and you can converse in there any time you wish.

iMessage

iMessage is a special term used for text messages exchanged between people who use Apple devices. For instance, you may notice when texting certain people that your messages will appear as blue (<u>Figure 8.3</u>). Conversely, you will notice when texting other people that your messages will appear as green (<u>Figure 8.4</u>). When they appear blue, that means you are sending iMessages to each other. In other words, you both are using Apple devices such as an iPhone, iPad, or Mac to send your text messages. iMessages (blue) are different because they are not sent as cellular text messages. In other words, they do not count against your text message count if your cellular plan limits them. Also, when you are conversing with someone using iMessage, there are additional options available to you, which we will now cover.

Figure 8.3 – iMessage Example

Figure 8.4 – Regular Text Message

Sharing Photos with Messages

There are a ton of special effects and add-ons you can use with the Messages app (Figure 8.5). For instance, if you want to text message a picture to someone, tap the Photos app icon underneath the message bar. Now you can browse through your saved photos on the bottom by swiping left and right, and you can send one of those photos by tapping on a photo and then tapping the send icon. You can also browse through all your photos to send by tapping on All Photos.

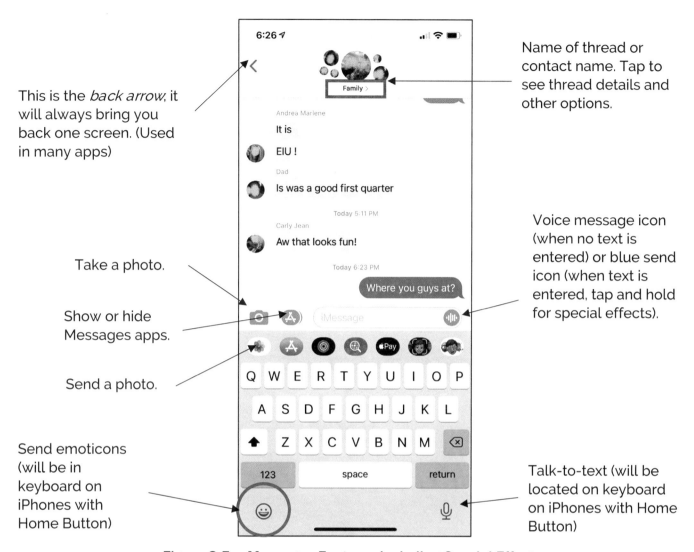

This is the *back arrow*, it will always bring you back one screen. (Used in many apps)

Name of thread or contact name. Tap to see thread details and other options.

Take a photo.

Show or hide Messages apps.

Send a photo.

Voice message icon (when no text is entered) or blue send icon (when text is entered, tap and hold for special effects).

Send emoticons (will be in keyboard on iPhones with Home Button)

Talk-to-text (will be located on keyboard on iPhones with Home Button)

Figure 8.5 – Messages Features including Special Effects

Alternatively, you can take a picture right now to send by tapping on the camera icon at the left of the message bar.

Special Effects with Messages

There are many special effects you can send with Messages. We will not cover all of them in here, but you can send emoticons by tapping on the smiley face on your keyboard. You can also send voice messages to the thread by using the microphone icon to the right of the message bar, which will only appear when no text is entered into the message bar. Another useful tool is talk-to-text, which allows you to speak your message to your iPhone and it will type it out for you. To use talk-to-text, tap on the microphone icon at the very bottom right of your screen (or in your keyboard is you have an **iPhone with a home button**).

Screen & Text Effects

Screen and text effects are visual effects that are sent along with your text message. They can only be sent when using iMessage (i.e., texting a fellow Apple user). Here is how to send a screen or text effect:

1. Type in a text message but do not send it.
2. Instead of tapping the blue send icon, tap and **hold** the blue send icon.
3. A new screen will appear (Figure 8.6).

Tap to view bubble effects.

Tap to view full screen effects.

Tap on the blue send icon to send it out.

Tap to cancel and exit special effects.

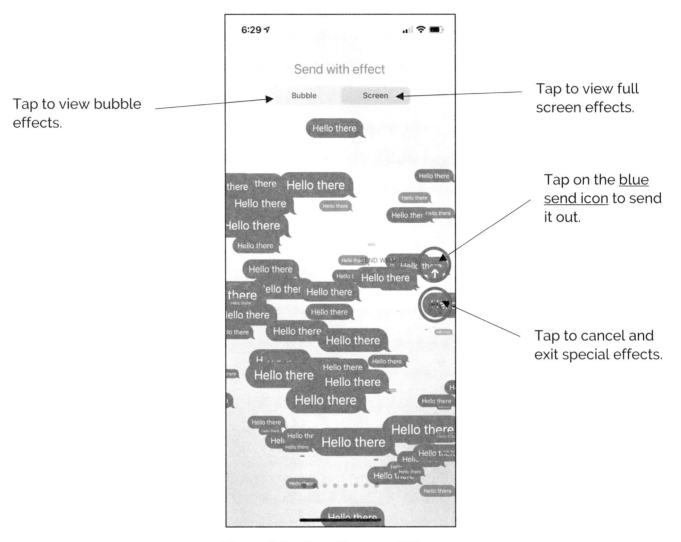

Figure 8.6 – Text Message Effects

4. To add a text effect, otherwise known as a bubble effect, you can tap on one of the options to the right. The effect will preview as you tap on it. To send the effect, after tapping on it tap on the small blue send icon next to the effect.
5. To add a full screen effect, tap on the Screen box at the top. Now you can swipe left and right to preview different screen effects. To send the full screen effect, tap the small blue upwards arrow icon next to the effect name. (Figure 8.6)
6. You can cancel sending an effect by tapping on the x icon.

Managing Messages

An important aspect of messages is managing them. Let us look at a couple key management features that are helpful to know.

How to Delete Threads

You can delete an entire thread by following these steps:

1. Open the Messages app.
2. Tap Edit at the upper left.
3. Tap Select Messages.
4. Tap each thread you want to delete, until they are check-marked.
5. Tap Delete at the lower right.

How to Delete Individual Texts

1. Open a thread in the Messages app.
2. Find the exact text you want to delete and tap and hold on it until some options appear. (Figure 8.7)
3. Tap More… at the bottom.
4. Now you can tap each individual text within a thread to be check-marked that you want deleted.

5. Tap the trash icon at the lower left to delete the selected texts.

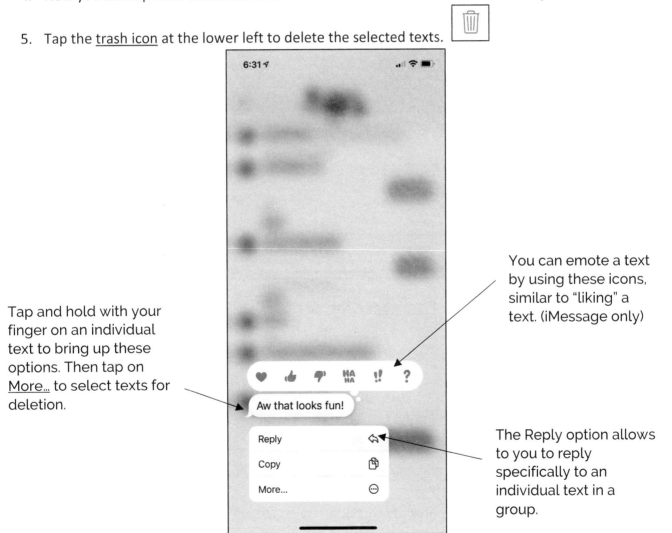

Tap and hold with your finger on an individual text to bring up these options. Then tap on More… to select texts for deletion.

You can emote a text by using these icons, similar to "liking" a text. (iMessage only)

The Reply option allows to you to reply specifically to an individual text in a group.

Figure 8.7 – Managing Individual Text Messages

Thread Details

Thread details offer a glimpse into certain information about a thread, such as who is in the thread, and any pictures exchanged in the thread. To access thread information, simply open a thread in Messages, and then tap the *name of the thread* at the top, and then tap the info icon. (Figure 8.8)

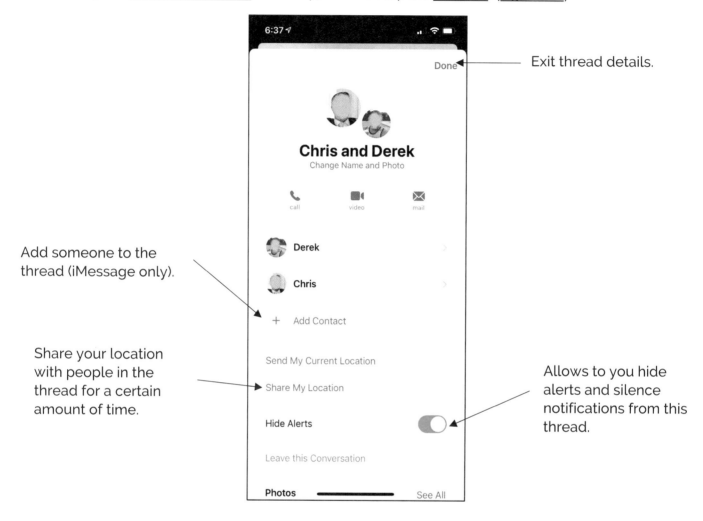

Figure 8.8 – Thread Details

Pinned Threads

Pinned threads are conversations that you can "pin" to the top of your Messages app for easy access (see Figure 8.1). These pinned threads will always remain at the top of the Messages app and you can access them by tapping on it. To pin or unpin a thread, follow these steps:

1. Inside the Messages app, tap and hold on a *thread* until a popup screen appears (Figure 8.9).
2. Tap Pin inside this popup box (Figure 8.9).
3. To remove a pinned thread, follow the step 1 but on an already pinned thread, and then tap Unpin.

TIP: To quickly pin a message thread, tap on the thread and swipe your finger slightly to the right until you see a yellow pin icon. Now tap on this <u>yellow pin icon</u> and the thread will become pinned.

Tap to "pin" the thread to the top of the Messages app.

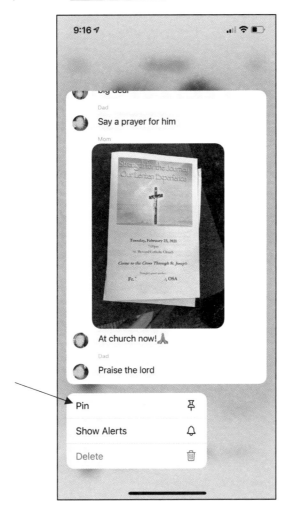

Figure 8.9 – How to Pin a Thread

Messages Apps

There are apps you can download that specifically work with the Messages app on your iPhone, and as you download apps later you will see them automatically appear while in a thread. Some of these apps can be very useful while using the Messages app. To view the apps you currently have available within Messages, tap on the <u>App Store icon</u> while in a thread (<u>Figure 8.5</u>). Now you can see what apps you currently have within Messages. Your iPhone will come preloaded with apps you can use with Messages, such as the Photos app which we have already used to demonstrate how to send a photo to someone within a text message. We will not cover the various apps available for Messages, but they are worth playing around with at your leisure. I would especially recommend checking out the <u>Animoji app</u> (monkey face) and <u>#images app</u> (magnifying glass). Both apps are fun to use and are even mentioned in the tips and tricks chapter of this book. Some of these apps may not be available on all iPhones

Chapter 9 – Email

Your iPhone can seamlessly manage your email accounts. It is quite convenient when you can quickly reply to an email in 10 seconds straight from your iPhone. All your emails and email accounts are located within the Mail app, which we will get to shortly. For now, let us start by adding your existing email account to your iPhone.

Adding an Email Address to iPhone

1. Open the Settings app.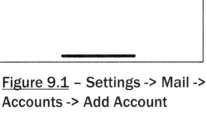
2. Find the Mail option and tap on it.
3. Tap Accounts.
4. Tap Add Account.
5. Look through the list of pre-populated email accounts such as AOL, Google (Gmail), and Yahoo. If you have one of these accounts, tap on it. If your account does not appear, tap on Other. (Figure 9.1)
6. If you tapped on a pre-populated account, follow the instructions that appear on your screen. Most likely you will just have to enter in your email address and password. If you tapped on Other, tap on Add Mail Account. (Figure 9.2)

Figure 9.1 – Settings -> Mail -> Accounts -> Add Account

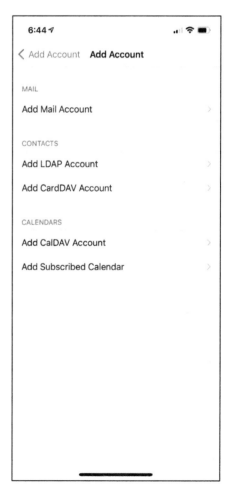

Figure 9.2 – Tap Add Mail Account for standard email addresses, if you chose Other.

61

7. Now type in the requested information. When done, tap <u>Next</u> at the upper right. (<u>Figure 9.3</u>)

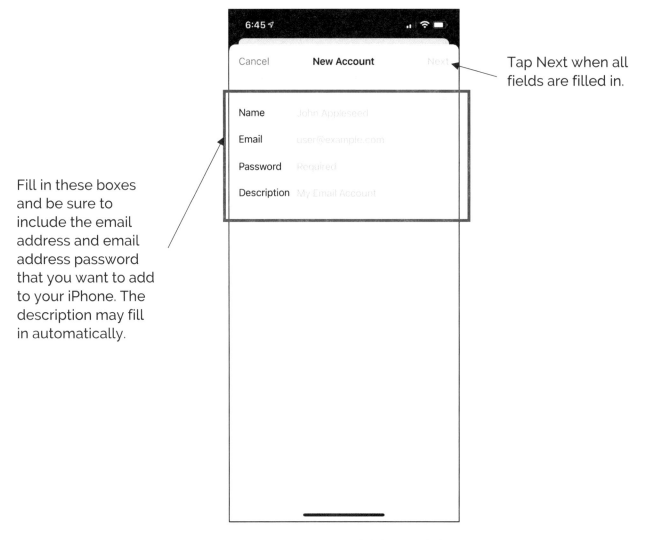

Tap Next when all fields are filled in.

Fill in these boxes and be sure to include the email address and email address password that you want to add to your iPhone. The description may fill in automatically.

<u>Figure 9.3</u> – Enter your Email Address Information Here

8. Your iPhone will attempt to add your email account given the information you provided. For most email accounts, this should work with no issues. However, for less common email accounts, your iPhone may require more information such as incoming and outgoing server addresses. If this is the case for you, you will have to contact your email provider to get this information.
9. Continue following the instructions that appear on your screen until you have reached the end. You can continue by tapping on <u>Next/Done/Save</u> at the upper right.

Once your email account has successfully been added, you are ready to use email on your iPhone. You can add multiple email addresses to your iPhone if you wish.

Checking Your Email

To check your email, we need to use the <u>Mail app</u>, which is located somewhere on your home screen. Tap on it to open it up.

Your email accounts will now be listed (<u>Figure 9.4</u>). You can use the <u>back arrow</u> at the upper left to view all your email accounts. Simply tap on an account to view your emails for that specific account.

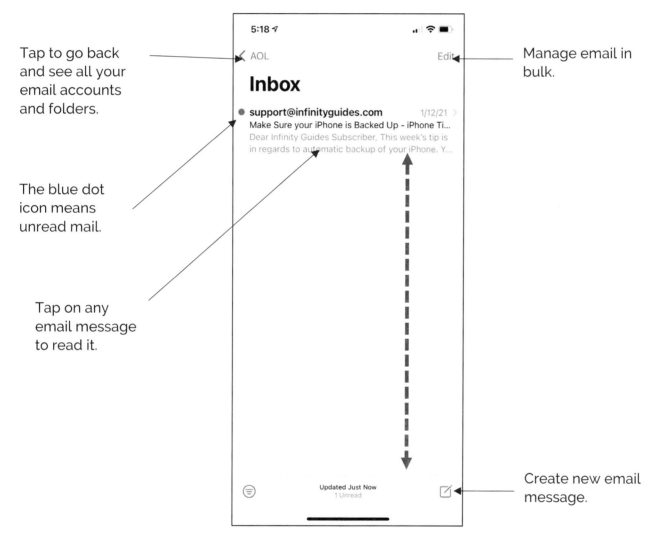

Tap to go back and see all your email accounts and folders.

The blue dot icon means unread mail.

Tap on any email message to read it.

Manage email in bulk.

Create new email message.

<u>Figure 9.4</u> – The Mail App

Viewing Email

To view an email, simply tap on it and it will appear full screen (Figure 9.5).

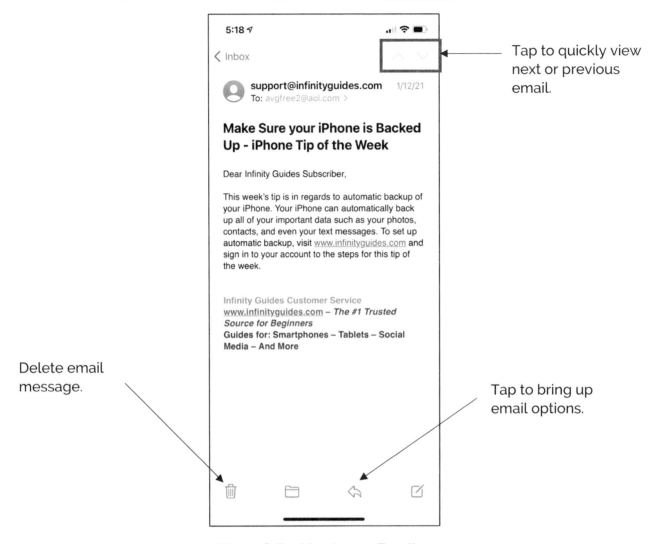

Tap to quickly view next or previous email.

Delete email message.

Tap to bring up email options.

Figure 9.5 – Viewing an Email

From here you have several options available to you if you tap on the arrow icon (Figure 9.5). Looking at the icons at the bottom of your screen, they perform the following by tapping on them (Figure 9.6).

- **Flag** – Flags or marks the message.
- **Move Message** – Moves the message to a different folder.
- **Trash** – Deletes or Archives the message (Different icon for Gmail accounts).
- **Arrow** – Replies, forwards, or replies to all.
- **Print** – Prints the email to a network printer

You can use the x icon to close the options and then the back arrow at the upper left to go back to all your emails.

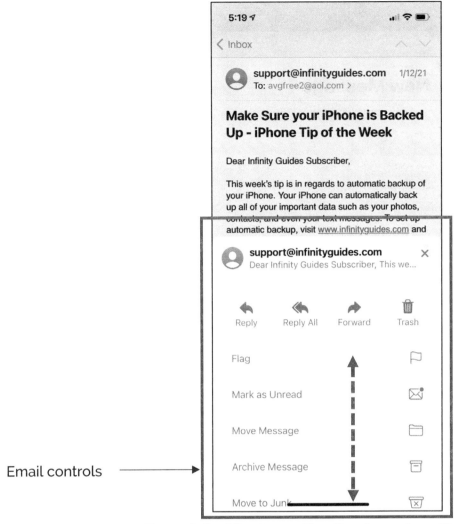

Figure 9.6 – Viewing an Email -> Arrow Icon (Options)

Sending Email

At any time from the Mail app, you can create a new email by tapping the <u>square and pencil icon</u> at the lower right. This will bring up a new message box. Full steps are (<u>Figure 9.7</u>):

1. Tap the <u>square and pencil icon</u> at the lower right inside the <u>Mail app</u> (<u>Figure 9.4</u>).
2. Enter in the email address or contact name of the intended recipient. Use the <u>+</u> icon to search through your contacts.
3. Tap into the <u>subject line</u>, and type in the subject.
4. Tap into the <u>message body</u>, and type in the email message.
5. Tap the <u>send arrow icon</u> at the upper right to send the message; or tap <u>Cancel</u> at the upper left to cancel the message.

Enter recipient email address.

Enter email subject.

Enter email message.

Tap to send.

Tap to search your contact list.

Figure 9.7 – Composing New Email

Managing Email

To Delete Email(s)

1. Tap an email account or folder to view all emails in that category.
2. Tap Edit at the upper right.
3. Tap each email you want to manage. If you want to select all, tap on Select All at upper left.
4. Use the text at the bottom to manage. Tap on Mark, Move, or Archive/Delete/Trash.
5. To cancel, tap Cancel at the upper right.

TIP: You can quickly delete an individual email by tapping on its preview, then swiping to the left.

Chapter 10 – Web Browsing

One of the signature features of the iPhone is the ease in which you can surf the web. To access the Internet, open the Safari app on your home screen. Safari is where you will be doing all your internet

browsing unless you download a different app to browse the web.

Visiting Web Pages

Safari is Apple's web browser optimized for the iPhone. In Safari, you can visit web pages as well as search the web using your favorite search engine. By default, Google is set as the current search engine. To search the web, tap in the box at the top of the screen and type in your search parameters, then touch go on your keyboard. If you want to visit a webpage directly, touch in the same box and type in the web address, followed by tapping go. (Figure 10.1)

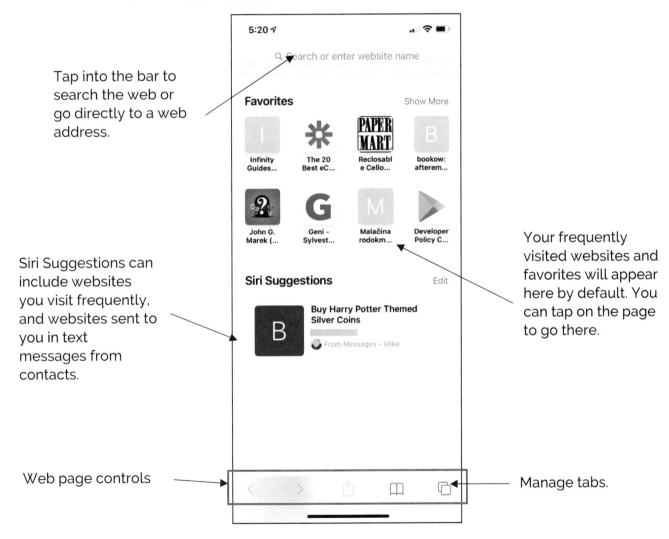

Figure 10.1 – Safari: Search Web & Visit Websites

67

Navigating the web on the iPhone is a unique experience and takes some practice. Think of your finger as the mouse pointer and touching down on the screen as a click. To open a link, simply touch down on it with your finger (Figure 10.2).

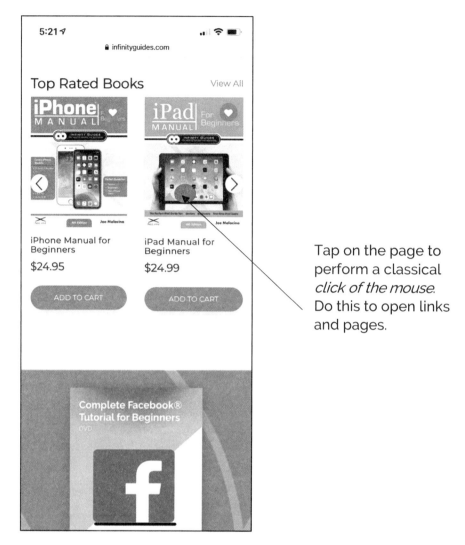

Tap on the page to perform a classical *click of the mouse*. Do this to open links and pages.

Figure 10.2 – Safari: Tap to Click (Open Pages)

Scrolling through web pages works the same way as scrolling through apps. Simply drag your finger up and down to scroll through a web page. If you need to zoom in on something, there is a simple way. To zoom in on a very specific section of a web page, touch down on the screen with two fingers, with your two fingers being very close together. Then spread your fingers apart while remaining on the screen. To zoom back out, touch two fingers down on the screen again, only this time have the fingers start far apart, and pull the fingers in towards each other. (Figures 10.3 & 10.4)

To zoom out: touch down on the screen with TWO fingers, with the fingers spaced far apart. Then drag the two fingers together while remaining on the screen. Release when the fingers come together, or when you are satisfied with the zoom.

Figure 10.3 – Safari: Zooming Out

To zoom in: touch down on the screen with TWO fingers, with the two fingers being close together. Then drag the fingers away from each other in opposite directions while remaining on the screen, releasing at the end or when you are satisfied with the zoom.

Figure 10.4 – Safari: Zooming In

You can still do all the basic functions of your normal web browser with Safari. To browse through basic web functions, touch down at the bottom of your screen. This will bring up Safari navigation options also known as web page controls (See Figure 10.1). From here, you can browse as you please. For instance, to go back to the previous page, touch the left arrow. To go forward a page, touch the right arrow. To manage a webpage, touch the rectangle with the arrow inside it. From here you have the options to mail the webpage to a friend, message the page to a friend, tweet the page on your Twitter (if Twitter app installed), share the page to Facebook (if Facebook app installed), add a shortcut to the web page to your home screen, print the web page, bookmark the page, or to add the page to your reading list (Figure 10.5). If you choose to bookmark the page, the page will appear in your bookmarks screen which can be accessed by touching the book icon at the bottom of Safari.

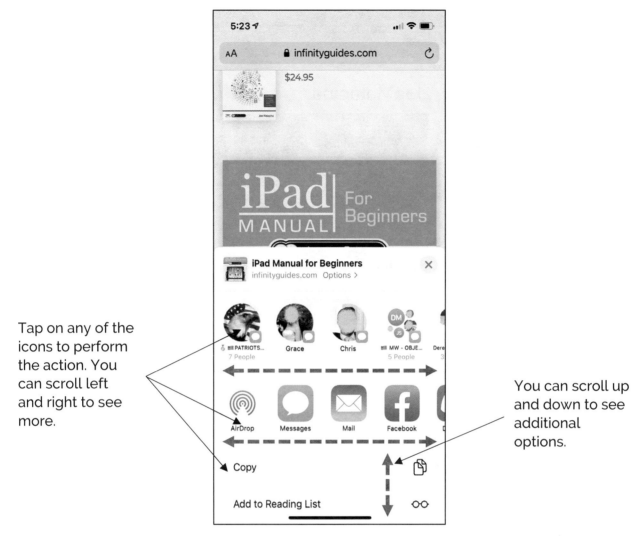

Tap on any of the icons to perform the action. You can scroll left and right to see more.

You can scroll up and down to see additional options.

Figure 10.5 – Safari: Managing a Web Page (Arrow & Rectangle Icon)

Finally, you can browse in multiple tabs in Safari by tapping the two windows icon at the bottom right of the Safari screen and then touching the plus icon (Figure 10.6). Tabs are a multi-tasking tool that allow you to have multiple windows open in which you can browse the internet. To browse between tabs, touch the windows icon again. To truly master browsing through Safari, just take some time playing with it, and you will get it in no time.

Tap the x or swipe the page off the screen to close a tab.

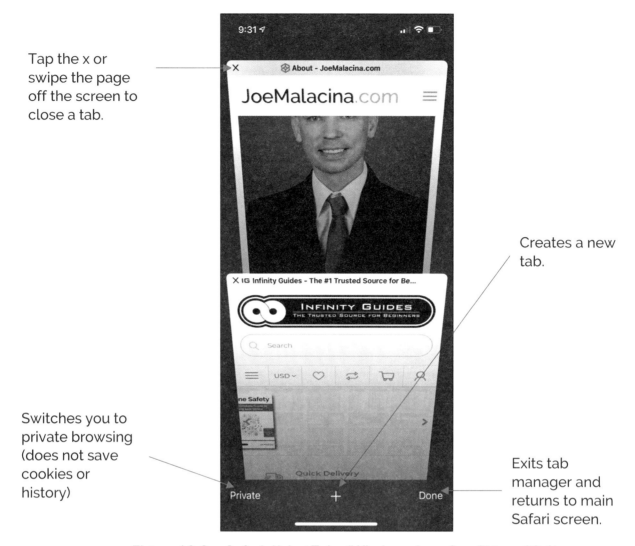

Creates a new tab.

Switches you to private browsing (does not save cookies or history)

Exits tab manager and returns to main Safari screen.

Figure 10.6 – Safari: Using Tabs (Windows Icon-See Figure 10.1)

Chapter 11 – Using your Camera

The iPhone is equipped with a powerful camera with flash capability. To access the camera, touch the Camera app on your home screen. There are a few options available inside the Camera app. To access all these options, tap on the arrow icon at the top of your screen. (Figure 11.1)

- **Lightning:** This turns flash to on, off, or auto.
- **Moon Icon:** This is the night mode indicator, which will enable and disable automatically.
- **Concentric Circles (if equipped):** This enables or disables LIVE photo, which captures a second or so before and after the photo, thus creating what is called a "live photo."
- **4:3 Icon** – Tapping on this icon allows you to change the aspect ratio.
- **+/- Icon** – Allows you to adjust the exposure of the lens.
- **Timer** – Tapping on this icon allows you to set a timer for the capture sequence.
- **Color Palette** – Allows you to choose a filter to capture the photo.

Taking a Photo

To take a photo, aim your camera and then tap on the large circle icon at the bottom of your screen. You can also turn your iPhone to the side to take a picture in landscape mode. In addition, you can change the zoom by tapping on the appropriate magnification. Lastly, you can use the selfie lens, which faces directly back at you, by tapping on the circular arrows icon at the lower right of your screen. (Figure 11.1)

Camera Modes

You can switch between different camera modes by first tapping on the arrow icon at the top of your screen to hide the camera options. Then you can tap down anywhere on your screen and swipe to the left and the right. You will notice different text become highlighted right above the capture icon to indicate which mode you are in.

The different modes are:

- **Photo** – Standard photo mode
- **Video** – Records a video.
- **Slo-Mo** – Records a video in slow motion.
- **Time-Lapse** – Records a time lapse sequence.
- **Portrait** – Ideal for taking professional portrait photos (Advanced).
- **Pano** – Captures a panoramic photo.

You can preview the photo you have just taken by tapping on the preview of the photo at the lower left of your screen. To get back to the camera from this preview, tap the back arrow at the upper left or tap on the photo and swipe down.

Tap to bring up camera options.

Tap on screen and swipe left or right to switch between camera modes.

Magnification options

Camera options

Switch between regular and selfie lens.

Recent Photo Preview (tap to open)

Capture Icon (tap to take picture or record video)

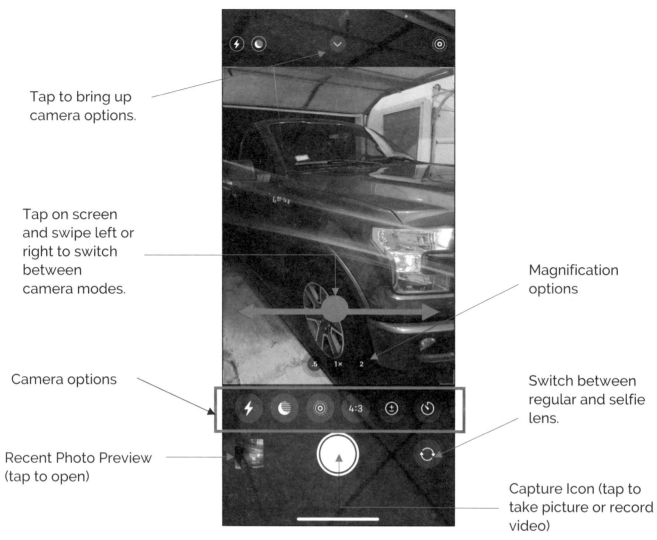

Figure 11.1 – Camera App

Chapter 12 – Photos & Videos

Now that we know how to take photos and record videos, it is time to learn what we can do with these. All your photos and videos can be found in the Photos app, which is located somewhere on your home

screen.

Photos App Layout

When you first open the Photos app, it may look like there is a lot going on (Figure 12.1). Let us look at navigating this expansive app. At the bottom will be your browsing tabs. The Library tab will show you all your photos in chronological order. You can browse through these by scrolling up and down and using the view options at the bottom. For You will show some of your photos recommended by your iPhone as well as your recent activity. An example of this is a photo you took one year ago from today. The Albums tab will bring you to all your albums. Lastly, the Search tab allows you to search through your photos. While browsing through your photos, at any time you can view a photo in full screen by tapping on it.

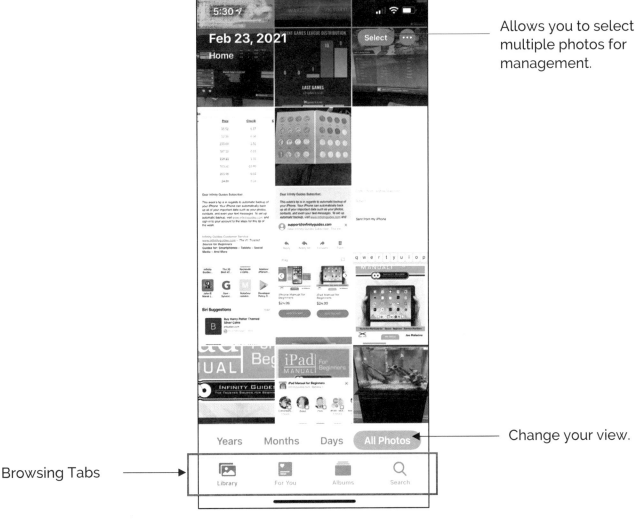

Allows you to select multiple photos for management.

Change your view.

Browsing Tabs

Figure 12.1 – Photos App -> Library Tab

iCloud Photos

Before we explore the Photos app more thoroughly, it is important to discuss what is called iCloud Photos. Photos take up a lot of storage space on your iPhone. Videos take up even more space. Your iPhone is equipped with what is called iCloud Photos, which basically stores your photos off your iPhone and in the cloud, which is just a hard drive that is stored on the internet. iCloud Photos may be a great option for you if you plan on keeping many photos on your iPhone. To use iCloud Photos your Apple ID must be set up, which we covered at the beginning of this book. If you want to enable iCloud Photos, follow these steps:

1. Open the Settings app.
2. Find Photos and tap it.
3. At the top, tap the indicator icon to the right of iCloud Photos to enable it (green will show).
4. Choose whether you want to Optimize iPhone Storage or Download and Keep Originals. (Optimize storage will save you space)
5. You will now be using iCloud Photos.

It may take some time for your iPhone to upload all your photos into the cloud.

Browsing Photos

Back inside the Photos app, let us look around. The two best tabs at the bottom for browsing photos are Library and Albums. If you tap on the Library tab, all your photos will be sorted by date. You can use the bottom view options to change your view. A popular way to see all your photos is to select the All Photos option at the bottom, which will show you every photo you have taken, along with any photos you have saved or screenshotted. (Figure 12.1)

To view all your photo albums, tap on the Albums tab. From here you can open your Recents album, which will show you all the recent photos you have saved. To view a photo, tap on _it_ to bring it full screen. Use the back arrow at the upper left to go back. (Figure 12.2)

To Create an Album
(See Figure 12.2)

1. Tap the Albums tab in Photos.
2. Tap the plus sign at the upper left (If you do not see this, tap on Albums again).
3. Tap New Album (New Shared Album will create a photo album you can share with other Apple device users).
4. Type in your new album name and tap Save.
5. Scroll through your photos and tap each one you want to add to the album.
6. Once you have selected all the photos you want, tap Done at the upper right.

To Edit an Album
1. First, to view all your Albums go to the Albums tab and then tap on See All next to the text My Albums. (Figure 12.2)
2. Open the album you want to edit by tapping on _it_.
3. Tap Select at the upper right.
4. Tap each photo you want to manage within the album.

5. Use the options at the bottom of your screen.

Tap to create a new album.

Tap to see all your photo albums.

Tap to see all your recent photos.

Figure 12.2 – Photos App -> Albums Tab

Sharing a Photo

To share a photo, follow these steps (Figure 12.3):

1. Find the photo you want to share and tap on *it* to bring it full screen. (Note: You can select multiple photos by tapping Select at the upper right).
2. Tap the rectangle with the arrow inside it at the lower left.
3. Tap on the corresponding option as to how you want to share it (Message, Mail, Facebook, etc.).

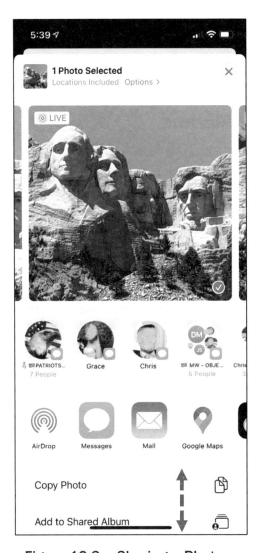

Figure 12.3 – Sharing a Photo

Deleting Photos

1. Tap on the *photo* you want to delete (or select multiple by tapping on <u>Select</u> at the upper right).
2. Tap the <u>trash icon</u> at the lower right to delete.

Editing a Photo

You can edit a photo in multiple ways, here is how:

1. Tap on the _photo_ you want to edit to bring it full screen.
2. Tap Edit at the upper right. (Figure 12.4)

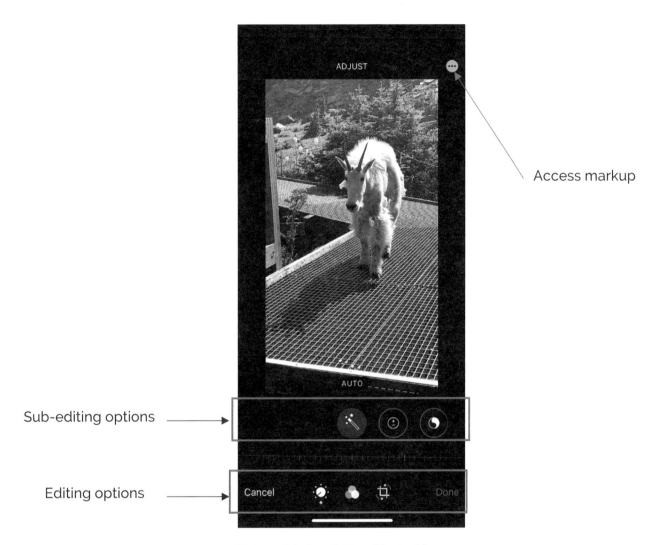

Figure 12.4 – Edit a Photo Menu

a. You can crop the photo by tapping on the <u>crop icon</u> at the bottom of your screen. Then use your fingers and drag the border to determine the crop. You can rotate the photo using the <u>block and arrow icon</u>. (<u>Figure 12.5</u>)

Rotate photo.

Tap and drag the corners of the picture until your desired crop has been reached. Tap <u>Done</u> when finished editing.

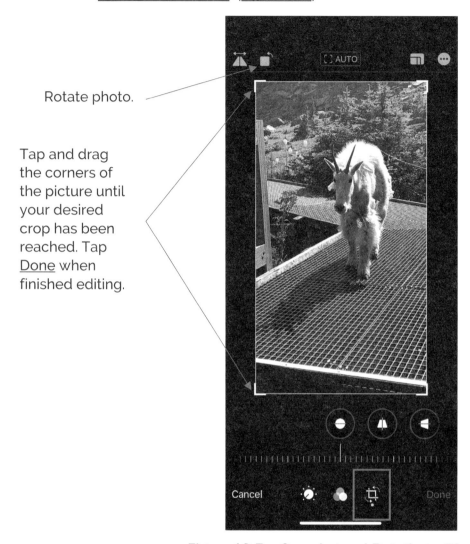

<u>Figure 12.5</u> – Cropping and Rotating a Photo

b. You can add a filter to the photo by tapping on the <u>color palette icon</u>. (<u>Figure 12.6</u>)

Tap on a filter choice to add the filter.

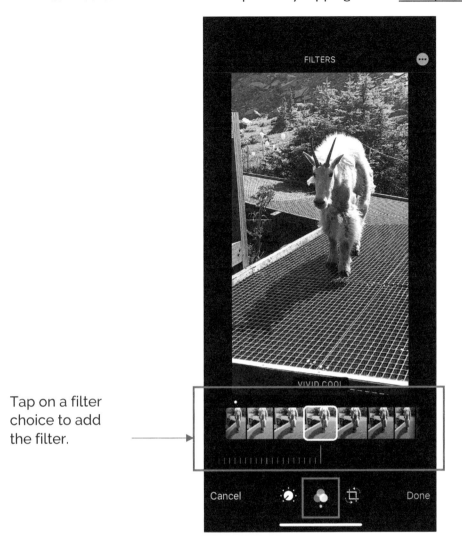

<u>Figure 12.6</u> – Adding a Filter to a Photo

c.   You can alter lighting and shading of the photo by tapping on the <u>sun icon</u>. (<u>Figure 12.7</u>)

Drag the slider to the desired setting.

<u>Figure 12.7</u> – Adjusting Lighting and Color Settings of a Photo

d. You can mark up the photo by tapping on <u>the 3 dots within the circle icon</u>. Tap <u>Markup</u>. (<u>Figure 12.8</u>)

Using markup, you can write directly on the picture by placing your finger on the photo and drawing with your finger.

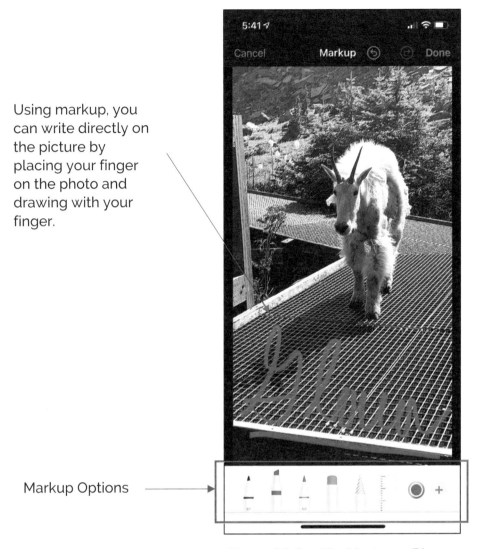

Markup Options

<u>Figure 12.8</u> – Marking up a Photo

e. Tap Done when finished with Markup.

3. Tap <u>Done</u> on your screen when you are done editing the photo.

Shared Photo Albums

A Shared Photo Album allows you to share an album with your friends who use Apple devices. To create a new Shared Album:

1. Tap the <u>Albums tab</u> at the bottom inside the <u>Photos app</u>.
2. Tap the <u>+</u> sign at the upper left.
3. Tap <u>New Shared Album</u>.
4. Name your shared album.
5. Tap <u>Next</u> in the box.
6. Enter in the contacts you want to share the album with one at a time. NOTE: They must be Apple Device users.
7. Tap <u>Create</u> when done.
8. A notification will be sent to all the contacts you entered.
9. Now tap on the *new shared album* you created. From here, you can add photos to the album by tapping the <u>plus symbol</u>.

When you receive an invitation to a shared Photo Album, the Photos app will notify you and you can join the Shared Album from the <u>For You</u> tab.

Chapter 13 – iPhone Security

Security is a very important feature of the iPhone. As I emphasized early on in this book, it is extremely important to remember your lock screen passcode. If you forget this passcode, it is extremely tedious to get back into your device. Doing so actually involves resetting your device to factory conditions, which will delete all your data. In this chapter I will show you how to change the security settings of your iPhone, including your lock screen passcode. Also, please remember your lock screen passcode is different from your Apple ID password.

Settings

All your security settings can be viewed and changed inside the Settings app. We have used the Settings app several times already in this book so you should have no problem by now finding and opening it. As a reminder, the Settings app can be found on your home screen, and you can open it by tapping on it with your finger.

Here inside the Settings app is where you can alter all the under the hood aspects of your iPhone. We will explore more in Settings later, but for now, locate Face ID & Passcode **[iPhones without Home Button]** or Touch ID & Passcode (Note: Older iPhones that do not have Touch ID capability will just show Passcode, you may have to look inside General in Settings to find it.) **[iPhones with Home Button]** and tap on it.

Note: All iPhones without a home button have Face ID, whereas most iPhones with a home button have Touch ID. Some older iPhones do not have Touch ID, such as the iPhone 5c.

To get into Face/Touch ID & Passcode you will have to enter your current passcode. You may have set one up when you first set up your iPhone. Enter in your passcode and you will be brought to a new screen.

In this new screen you can alter many settings. You can choose whether to use Face/Touch ID, change your passcode, or even turn your passcode off. Let us explore these. (Figure 13.1 & Figure 13.2)

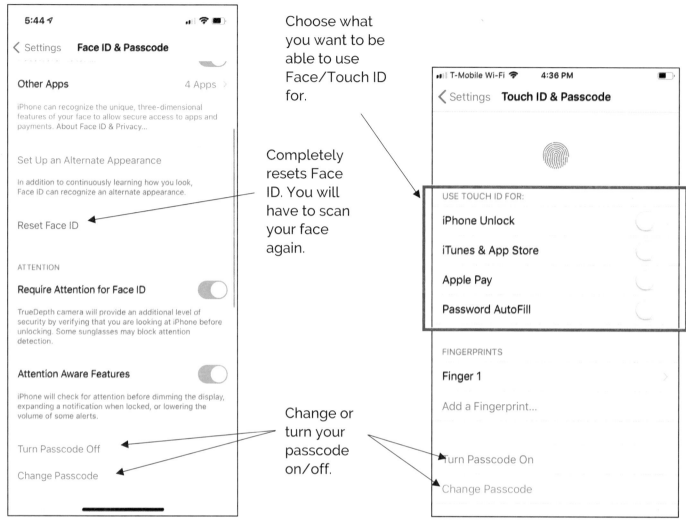

Figure 13.1 [iPhones without Home Button] – Settings -> Face ID & Passcode

Figure 13.2 [iPhones with Home Button] – Settings -> Touch ID & Passcode

Face ID (iPhones without Home Button only)

Face ID is one of the signature features of the iPhone, and it allows you to use your face to unlock it. It also allows you to use your facial scan for some other security measures, such as confirming a purchase of an app or song. When you first set up your iPhone, you were asked to set up Face ID. To use Face ID to unlock your iPhone from the sleep state, simply tap the screen to turn it on and then perform a home swipe (Go Home) and look at your iPhone until the unlock symbol appears at the top (Figures 13.3.1 and 13.3.2).

Indicates the iPhone is locked, and you must use Face ID or your passcode to unlock it.

Indicates the iPhone is unlocked (after Face ID), and you can perform a <u>home swipe</u> to access your home screen.

Figure 13.3.1 – Lock Screen, iPhone Locked

Figure 13.3.2 – Lock Screen, iPhone Unlocked (After using Face ID)

Once your iPhone is unlocked, if you already performed a home swipe you will be brought to your home screen. If you have not yet performed a <u>home swipe</u>, you can do so to access your home screen. If Face ID fails, you will be asked to enter your passcode to unlock your iPhone. You will also need your passcode whenever you restart your iPhone.

*Please note that when you use Face ID, you will still be required to have a passcode set as well. This passcode will be required whenever your restart your iPhone or if Face ID fails.

Setting up Face ID (iPhones without Home Button only)

As I briefly mentioned, when you first set up your iPhone, you were prompted to set up Face ID. If you have not done so or want to reset Face ID because it is not working to your standards, here is how:

How to Setup Face ID

1. Open the <u>Settings</u> app.
2. Tap <u>Face ID & Passcode</u>.

3. If prompted, enter your current Passcode.
4. Tap <u>Reset Face ID</u> if you want to reset it or <u>Set Up Face ID</u> if you want to turn it on.
5. Follow the instructions on your screen to set up Face ID. You will have to look directly at your iPhone's screen and move your head around in a circle twice.
6. Once complete, Face ID will be set up and ready to use.
7. If you previously did not set up a passcode, you will be required to do so when using Face ID.

How to Turn Face ID Off

1. Open the <u>Settings</u> app.
2. Tap <u>Face ID & Passcode</u>.
3. If prompted, enter your current Passcode.
4. Tap <u>Reset Face ID</u> to turn Face ID off.
5. Alternatively, you can turn Face ID off for certain functions by using the options at the top of your screen and disabling them (See <u>Figure 13.2</u>).

Touch ID (iPhones with Home Button only)

Touch ID allows you to use your fingerprint to unlock your device. It also allows you to use your fingerprint for some other security measures, such as confirming a purchase of an app or song. To turn on and use Touch ID, if you have not done so already when you first set up your iPhone, follow these steps. (If you already use Touch ID, you can use these steps to add an additional finger). From within Settings -> Touch ID & Passcode:

1. Tap <u>Add a Fingerprint</u>.
2. Now follow the instructions on the screen.
3. Once it is done, tap <u>Complete/Continue</u> at the bottom.
4. Your fingerprint will now be valid to unlock your device.

*Please note that when you use Touch ID, you will still be required to have a passcode set as well. This passcode will be required whenever your restart your iPhone or if Touch ID fails.

To use Touch ID to unlock your iPhone from the sleep state, first press the <u>home button (Go Home)</u>, then place your finger on the <u>home button</u> to use Touch ID. This will unlock your device and bring you to your home screen. If you do not have Touch ID, you will instead be prompted to enter your passcode once you press the home button.

Passcode

Your passcode is a password that allows you to unlock your iPhone in addition to Face/Touch ID. Unlocking is simply the process of getting into your iPhone to use it. A passcode is required to use Face/Touch ID, and if you choose not to use Face/Touch ID, I recommend setting up a passcode anyways. Otherwise, anyone will be able to get into your iPhone and have access to all of your data should they ever get possession of your iPhone and it does not have Face/Touch ID or a passcode set up.

Setting or Changing a Passcode

1. Within <u>Face/Touch ID & Passcode</u> in <u>Settings</u>, tap <u>Turn Passcode On</u> or <u>Change Passcode</u>.
2. If you are changing your passcode, you will be required to enter your current passcode. Do so.
3. Now you can enter a new passcode. The standard is a 6-digit passcode; however, many people prefer to use 4-digits or even an alphanumeric code. To change the type of passcode you want, tap on <u>Passcode Options</u>.
4. Now you can choose which type of passcode you want.
5. Tap in your new passcode.
6. Confirm the new passcode by tapping it in again.
7. Follow the instructions on your screen to finish entering your passcode.
8. When complete your passcode will be changed or set.

To Turn Off Passcode Completely

1. Within <u>Face/Touch ID & Passcode</u> in <u>Settings</u>, tap <u>Turn Passcode Off</u>.
2. Tap <u>Turn Off</u>
3. Enter in your current passcode. You also may be asked to enter in your Apple ID password for additional security purposes.
4. Please note that if you turn your passcode off completely, you will not be able to use Face/Touch ID.

As a final reminder, you can use your passcode to unlock your iPhone from the sleep state if your Face/Touch ID fails.

TIP: REMEMBER YOUR PASSCODE! Write it down somewhere safe and do not lose it! If you forget your passcode it is a very big headache to get back into your iPhone and you risk possibly losing all your data. If there is one tip I cannot emphasize enough it is this: **do not forget your passcode**.

Chapter 14 – Personal Settings

There are several personal settings you can set on your iPhone, and in this chapter, we will explore some of them.

Setting your Wallpapers

Your wallpaper is just the background image on your iPhone. You have 2 different wallpapers: your home screen and your lock screen. To set your wallpapers follow these steps:

1. Open the Settings app.
2. Tap Wallpaper.
3. Tap Choose a New Wallpaper.
4. You can now choose between Dynamic, Stills, Live, and one of your photos. Dynamic wallpapers are animated on your screen. Stills are not animated and are pre-loaded on the iPhone. Live wallpapers can become animated when you press down on them using Haptic Touch (More on Haptic Touch later). You can also select one of your current photos by browsing through your albums at the bottom. (Figure 14.1)

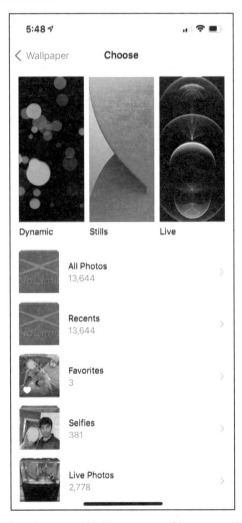

Figure 14.1 – Settings -> Wallpaper -> Choose a New Wallpaper

5. Select a photo to use as your wallpaper.
6. Now you can adjust the perspective zoom of the wallpaper if you wish (icon at the bottom in the middle). Enabling this adjusts your wallpaper to whichever angle you are viewing your iPhone at.
7. Tap Set.
8. Choose to set the wallpaper as your Lock Screen, Home Screen, or Both.

Ringtones & Vibrations

You can customize your ringtones and vibration settings in multiple ways. Here is how:

1. Open Settings.
2. Tap Sounds & Haptics.
3. Here you can adjust various sound settings such as ringer volume. To change a specific tone, such as your ringtone, tap on Ringtone.
4. Now you can tap on each tone to preview it on your iPhone. Once you have found the tone you want, use the back arrow at the upper left to go back.
5. You can adjust the vibration pattern of a tone by selecting the tone type (i.e., Ringtone) then tapping Vibration at the top.
6. Now you can tap each vibration pattern to preview it. Once you have found the pattern you like, use the back arrow at the upper left to go back.

Other Settings

You can adjust other personalized settings from within the Settings app. We will not cover them here in this text but feel free to check out Display & Brightness and Battery settings.

Chapter 15 – The Home Screen

By now, you should be familiar with your home screen. As a reminder, your home screen is the main screen of your iPhone that shows all your apps. You have multiple home screens, and you can switch between them by tapping down with your finger on the screen and swiping left or right. To get back to the main home screen at any time, simply <u>Go Home</u>. (See <u>Figure 4.1</u> in Chapter 4 as a reminder)

Haptic Touch

Haptic Touch, previously referred to as 3D Touch, is a feature on your iPhone that allows you to perform different functions while holding your finger down on the screen. Let us try it out and see what we can do.

Haptic Touch Example 1: On Apps

1. On your home screen, locate the <u>Messages</u> app.
2. Instead of tapping and releasing the Messages app to open it, tap down on it and hold until you feel a small haptic vibration and some options appear (<u>Figure 15.1</u>). Now release your finger. (This is called *Haptic Touch*). If you held on to the app for too long, all your apps will start to shake, in which case you should perform the <u>Go Home</u> action to cancel and try again.

By pressing down on the Messages app and holding for a moment, this screen will appear, allowing you to quickly go to a recent Messages thread.

<u>**Figure 15.1**</u> **– Haptic Touch on the Messages App**

3. The screen that appears shows some recent contacts you have exchanged text messages with. You can tap on any of their names to immediately be brought to that particular Messages thread.
4. You can return to your home screen by performing the Go Home action.

You can use Haptic Touch on just about every app. Try it out on other apps to see which shortcuts appear.

Haptic Touch Example 2: Photos

1. Open the Photos app.
2. Find a photo you want to quickly examine and instead of tapping on it normally, tap down and hold until you feel the haptic vibration and some options appear. Release your finger.
3. This will open a quick preview of the photo. If the photo is a Live Photo, it will play through it. Furthermore, if you selected a video, this would play the video.
4. The shortcuts that appear are useful, especially the copy function.

This is another example of how you can use Haptic Touch. Try using it within other apps as well.

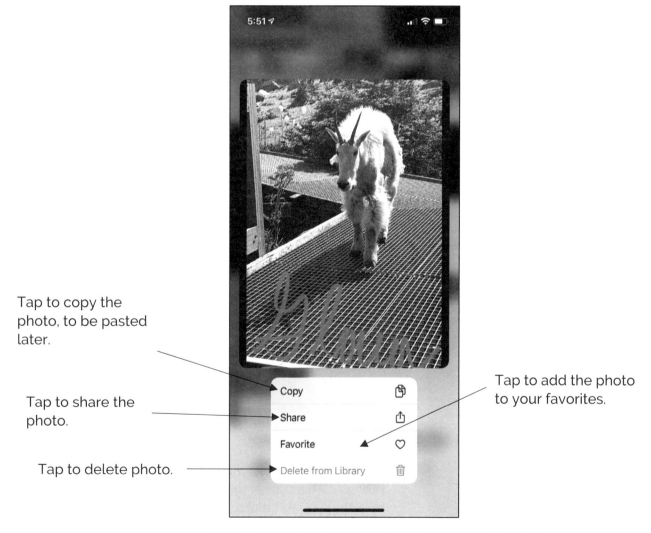

Tap to copy the photo, to be pasted later.

Tap to share the photo.

Tap to add the photo to your favorites.

Tap to delete photo.

Figure 15.2 – Haptic Touch on a Photo Thumbnail

Organizing Apps

Now that we learned how to use Haptic Touch, let us move on to how we can organize our home screens. On your home screens, you can choose where you want each app to appear. You can also group multiple apps together in a folder.

Moving Apps Around on your Home Screen (Figure 15.3)

1. Tap and hold down on an app on your home screen until all your apps start to shake, then release your finger. You may see a popup window while holding on an app; keep holding until all your apps start to shake. Alternatively, you can tap and hold on a blank area of your home screen.
2. Now that your apps are shaking, you can move the apps around.
3. To move an app, tap down on a shaking app and do not let go. You can now drag your finger anywhere on the screen to move the app to a new location.
4. To move the app to a new home screen, drag the app all the way to the right or left and hold it there, until the home screen changes. Go Home or tap Done at the upper right when you are finished.

Grouping Apps into Folders (Figure 15.3)

1. Tap and hold down on an app on your home screen until all your apps start to shake, then release your finger.
2. If you want to create a folder of apps on your home screen, tap down on an app and hold it, then drag it on top of another app that you want to group with the app you are holding.
3. You will see a small window appear behind your app. Release your finger.
4. A new folder has just been created. Your iPhone will name the folder for you. To change the name of the folder, tap into the *box* and use your keyboard to enter in a name.
5. Tap out of the folder to return to the home screen with your apps still shaking.
6. You can organize that folder the same way you can organize apps. You can move more apps into that folder by tapping, holding, and dragging apps into the folder. Go Home or tap Done at the upper right when you are finished.

How to Delete Apps (Figure 15.3)

1. Tap and hold down on an app on your home screen until all your apps start to shake, then release your finger.
2. To delete an app, tap the small minus symbol (-) that appears at the upper left of an app.
3. Then tap Delete.
4. To delete a folder, just move all the apps inside a folder out of that folder.
5. Please note that some apps that came with the iPhone cannot be deleted.
6. Once an app is deleted, you can get it back in the App Store, which is covered in the next chapter.
7. Go Home or tap Done at the upper right when you are finished.

Tap the "+" symbol to add widgets.

Tap the small "-" to delete the app.

Drag and drop with your finger one app to inside another app to create a folder on your home screen.

Drag and drop an app with your finger to another location on your home screen to move it there.

Drag an app with your finger to the edge of your screen to move it to another home screen.

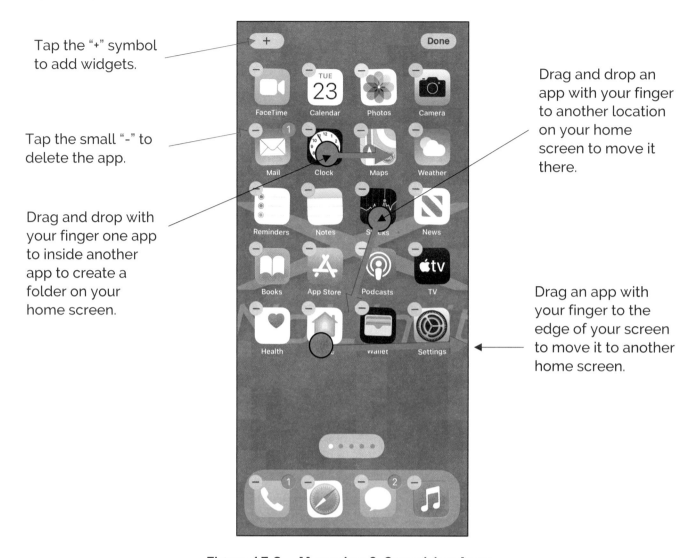

Figure 15.3 – Managing & Organizing Apps

Using Widgets

You can also add widgets to your home screen that can display information from apps in real-time. An example of this is the widget from the Stocks app which would show you stock quotes right on your home screen. Another example is the widget for the Weather app which can show you the 7-day forecast or hourly forecast. Widgets are a great way to quickly access a certain feature of an app. Here is how to add a widget to your home screen:

1. Tap and hold on a blank area of your home screen until all your apps start to shake and then release your finger.
2. Tap the plus sign at the upper left (Figure 15.3).
3. You are now brought to the widgets screen which allows you to find a widget to add to your home screen (Figure 15.4). Here you can scroll through different widgets available. Tap on one to begin adding it to your home screen.

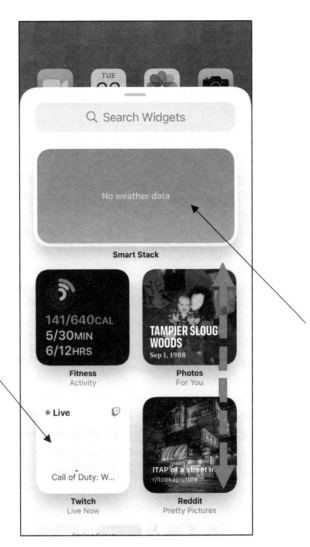

Tap on any widget to begin adding it to your home screen.

Tapping on this option will add a Smart Stack of widgets to your home screen.

Figure 15.4 – Adding Widgets to Home Screen

4. Next you can select how you want the widget to appear on your home screen, such as the information displayed and the size. To change this data, swipe left or right. When you have selected what you want, tap on Add Widget at the bottom of your screen (Figure 15.5).

Swipe left and right to choose between different widget options and different sizes.

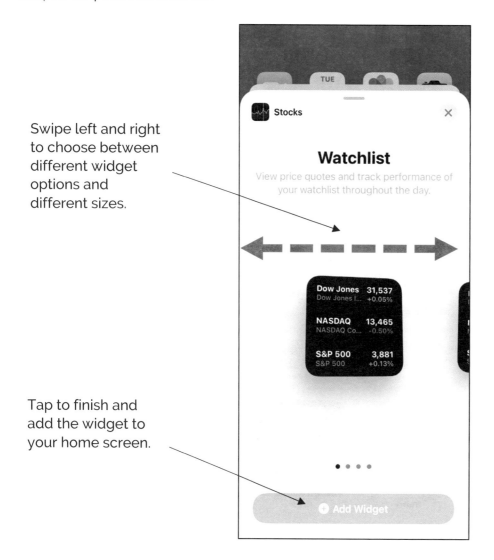

Tap to finish and add the widget to your home screen.

Figure 15.5 – Choosing Widget Options & Size

5. Your widget will now appear on your home screen. You can drag and drop the widget to an appropriate area of your screen the same way you can with an app. (Figure 15.6)
6. Tap Done at the upper right when you are finished.

The widget is now on your home screen.

Stacking Widgets and Smart Stack

Stacking widgets means putting multiple widgets together at the same place on your home screen. It is very similar to grouping apps together in a folder and is accomplished in the same exact way (see *Grouping Apps into Folders* earlier in this chapter). When you stack one widget on top of another, you can switch between these widgets by tapping on it and swiping up or down (Figure 15.6).

This is your new widget. You can move the widget the same way you can move apps. You can also place multiple widgets on top of one another in a stack.

You can swipe up and down on a stack of widgets to switch between the widgets. A Smart Stack will switch automatically throughout the day.

Figure 15.6 – Placing Widgets and Stacks

A Smart Stack is a stacked group of widgets that automatically rotate throughout the day to show you the most relevant information. For instance, a Smart Stack may show you the current weather when you first wake up, then the stock market during trading hours, and then some family photos before dinner. You can add a Smart Stack to your home screen from the Add Widgets screen (step 3 in *Using Widgets*).

App Library

The App Library is a page on your home screen that you can access by swiping your finger to the left several times until you reach the end. The App Library simply organizes your apps into different categories to help you find what you need. This is a great way to find an app that you know you have installed on your iPhone. In my opinion, a faster way to quickly locate an app on your home screen is to search for it by tapping the middle of your home screen and then swiping down.

Chapter 16 – Apps

All the things that your iPhone can do are functions of apps. When you make a phone call, you are using the Phone app. When you send a text message, you are using the Messages app. When you browse the Internet, you are using the Safari app. Even when you are changing your settings, you are using the Settings app. The apps that come with the iPhone are extraordinarily useful, but these are just a blade of grass in a prairie compared to the vast number of apps available. To get new apps, you will need to use an

app called the App Store, which is located somewhere on your home screen.

App Store

Let us open the App Store by tapping on it on our home screen. To use the App Store, you must have an Apple ID and you must be signed into your Apple ID on your iPhone. If you still have not set up your Apple ID yet, I strongly urge you to do so. See Chapter 5 on setting up your Apple ID.

Browsing the App Store

Here in the App Store (Figure 16.1) you can browse through the massive library of apps available for download. Again, make sure you are signed in with your Apple ID, and make sure you remember your Apple ID password as you may need it to download apps.

Here at the main page of the App Store, called the Today page, you can see all the new and featured apps that curators recommend. Let us look at the layout of this page and the App Store itself, particularly the tabs at the bottom.

- **Today** – The Today tab shows you featured apps and content.
- **Games** – This tab allows you to browse gaming apps.
- **Apps** – This tab allows you to browse through all apps available.
- **Arcade** – Brings you to Apple Arcade, which lets you play unlimited games for a monthly fee.
- **Search** – Allows you to search for a specific app or function of an app.

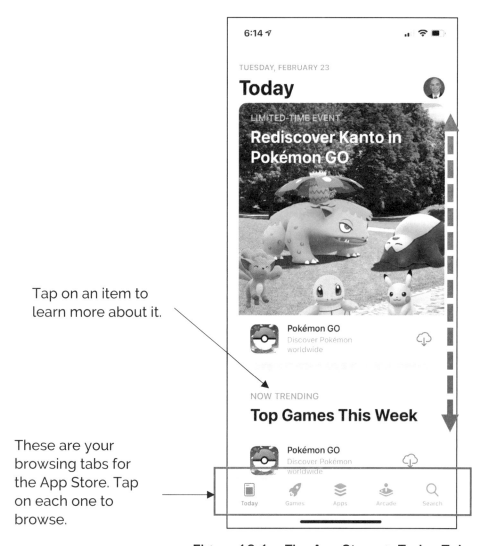

Tap on an item to learn more about it.

These are your browsing tabs for the App Store. Tap on each one to browse.

Figure 16.1 – The App Store -> Today Tab

Browsing by Category

One of the best ways to find good apps is to browse by category. To do this, first tap the <u>Apps</u> tab at the bottom, then scroll down until you see Top Categories (<u>Figure 16.2</u>). Some categories will be shown, and you can tap on one to explore it. For now, tap on <u>See All</u> to view all app categories.

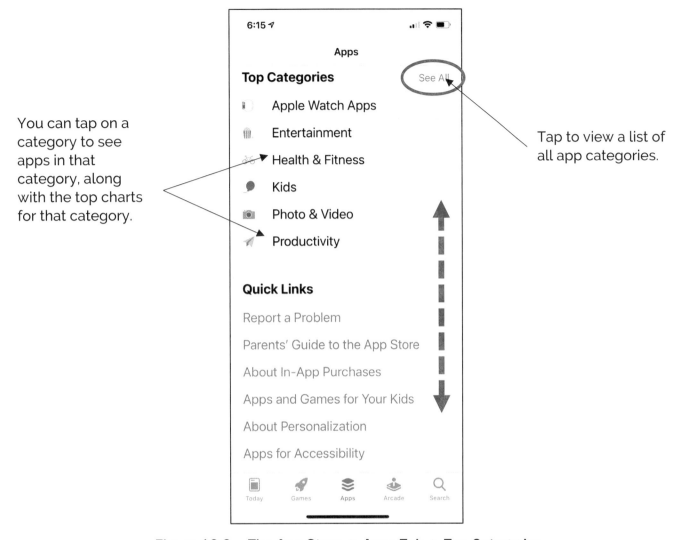

Figure 16.2 – The App Store -> Apps Tab -> Top Categories

When viewing all categories, you can scroll up and down to see the full list. Simply tap on a category to see the apps within it. Within each category page, you will see apps that are recommended by curators and the top charts for that category. The top charts include the most downloaded and used apps in that category and they are sorted by free apps and paid apps. Paid apps are apps you must pay for to download. As always, you can use the back arrows at the upper left to go back.

Viewing an App

(See Figure 16.3) When you see an app that interests you, you can tap on the app itself to view more information. On this screen you will see the name of the app, the price to download it if there is one, and you will see the app's user ratings, rankings, age recommendation, and more. By scrolling down and scrolling left and right you can see screenshots of the app, read a description of the app, and read user ratings and reviews.

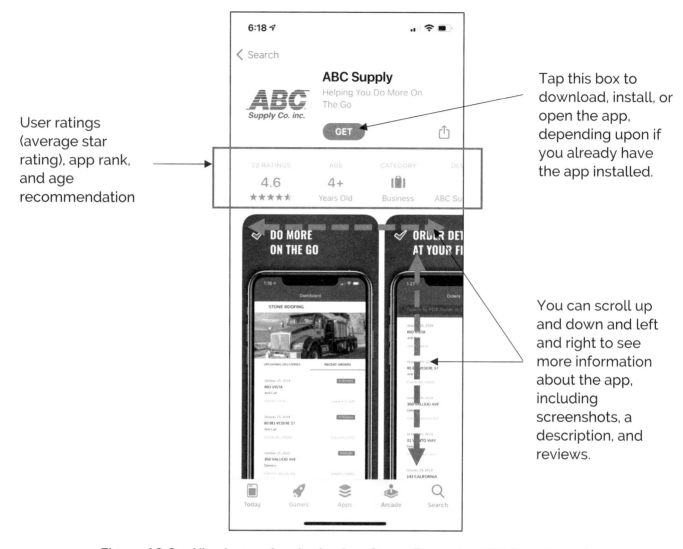

Figure 16.3 – Viewing an App in the App Store (Example: ABC Supply app)

Top Charts

Using Top Charts is one of my favorite ways to find popular apps. We have already briefly seen how to view Top Charts for categories, and this is one of the best ways to find great apps. To access these Top Charts, first make sure you are on the Apps tab. Then, scroll down until you come upon the Categories section again. Now tap on See All to view all categories. From here, tap on a category, such as Weather. Now you can scroll down until you see the headlines **Top Paid** and **Top Free**. These two sections show you the most downloaded and used paid and free apps in the Weather category. You can tap on See All to see the full list, and you can tap on any app to learn more information (Figure 16.4).

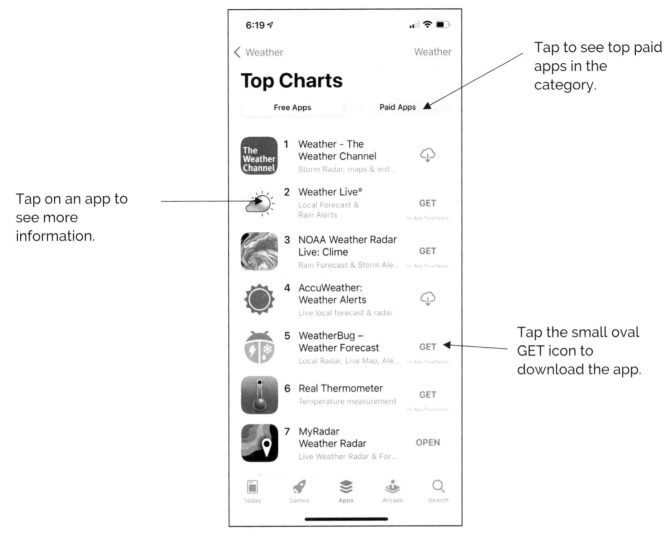

Tap to see top paid apps in the category.

Tap on an app to see more information.

Tap the small oval GET icon to download the app.

Figure 16.4 – The App Store -> Apps Tab -> Category -> Weather ->Top Charts (Free Apps)

Searching for Apps

If you know the specific app you want to download, you can search for it using the Search tab at the bottom. Tapping on this tab will allow you to search for any app by tapping into the search bar at the top of the screen. Simply type in the name of the app, or a subject such as "photo" and tap search on your keyboard. Usually, when you type the search term into the search field the App Store will make suggestions as to what you are looking for. You can tap on that suggestion to quickly enter it in and search. Now you will see a list returning your search results, and you can view these apps by tapping on them.

Downloading Apps

Now that we have seen how we can browse apps, let us see how we download one to our iPhone. The process is simple, but before we begin let me give a note on your Apple ID.

As emphasized earlier in this chapter, to use the App Store, you must be signed in with your Apple ID. You are also going to need your Apple ID password to download apps. On occasion, your iPhone will ask for this password just for verification purposes. Lastly, you will need credit card information linked to your

Apple ID to download certain apps. Adding your credit card information is easy. Your iPhone will ask you for it when it needs this information and will bring up a screen with instructions. Adding your credit card data does not mean you will be charged. The App Store just needs it IN CASE you decide to purchase something.

Here is how you download an app:

1. Open the App Store.
2. Find the app you want to download.
3. Next to the app will be a box. Inside this box will be the words GET or a price such as $0.99. If the box says OPEN, then you already have the app downloaded. (See Figure 16.4)
4. Tap this box.
5. You may be asked for your Apple ID password at this point or Face/Touch ID. Enter it in.
6. **[iPhones without Home Button]:** You may be asked to double press the sleep/wake button to proceed with your download. This is sometimes used to confirm a purchase. Do so if prompted and you want to go ahead with your download.
7. You may be asked to update your billing information at this point, such as credit card and billing address. Enter it in if prompted.
8. Your download will now commence. When it is finished, your newly downloaded app will appear on your home screen somewhere.

Using Downloaded Apps

When you download an app, it will appear on your home screen. To open it, just tap it. Using an app from the App Store is the same as any using any app that comes with the iPhone. You can usually scroll through screens on the app, tap icons, and more. Each app is unique to itself, so you will have to play around with the app to get the hang of it.

There are certain aspects of apps that are important to consider. The first is in-app purchases. Many apps allow you to buy features or items from directly inside the app. These purchases could be access to content or even physical goods. To make these purchases you may need to use your Apple ID. Another important aspect is advertisements. Some apps have advertisements running through them. For most apps these are non-conspicuous and do not interfere with using the app, but for others the advertisements can be quite bothersome. If an app is flooded with advertisements and popups that make it difficult to even use the app, I would consider deleting the app and using something else. Apps like these are just trying to spam you with advertisements rather than provide a good service.

It is also worth noting that some apps offer a paid and free version. Usually, the paid version comes with extra features or no advertisements.

Resources for Learning How to use Apps

You can check out the appendix of this text for a list of popular and useful apps. You might be amazed at what types of apps are out there and what they can do. For an additional resource on learning how to use apps, I recommend checking out www.infinityguides.com. Their website is dedicated to teaching people how to use many popular apps from a beginner's perspective.

Chapter 17 – Notifications

So far, we have covered all the bare basics of using the iPhone. You now know how to navigate the iPhone, make phone calls, exchange text messages, browse the Internet, use your email, personalize your device, download apps, and more. Now we are going to get into specific features that are essential to understand, and we start with notifications.

Overview

Notifications are an integral part of your iPhone. Every time you receive a text, you will receive a notification. Every time you miss a phone call, you will receive a notification. In fact, every time certain information is delivered to you from an app, you will receive what is called a notification.

Notifications appear on your iPhone in several forms. On your lock screen, you will see notifications lined up (Figure 17.1). While using your iPhone and it is unlocked, you will see notifications in real-time pop up at the top of your screen (Figure 17.2).

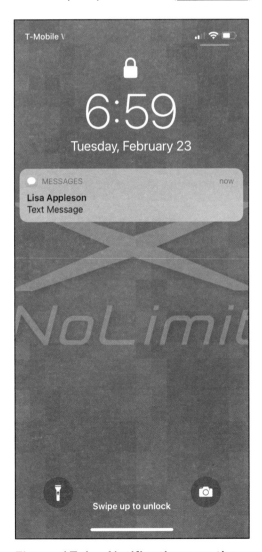

Figure 17.1 – Notifications on the Lock Screen

Figure 17.2 – Notifications on Home Screen

When these notifications appear, you can tap on it to be brought directly to the notification. For instance, if you receive a text message while you are doing something on your iPhone, a box will appear at the top of your screen showing the text message and who it is from. This box will appear briefly. While the box is there, you can tap on it to be brought directly into the thread of the text message so you can respond. Alternatively, you can tap that box and drag your finger down to reply immediately or tap the box and swipe it up to dismiss it.

Another type of notification is the badge icon, which is the red bubble you can see above an app on the home screen that has a number inside it. This usually means you have a certain number of notifications available for that particular app. For instance, your Messages app will show a number in a red bubble above it on your home screen. This number indicates how many unread text messages you currently have.

Notifications can also appear in real-time as an alert. An alert is a box that appears in the middle of your screen and they usually require you to dismiss the notification before it goes away. An example of this would be an emergency severe weather alert or something similar.

Notifications on the Lock Screen (iPhones without Home Button only)

When your iPhone is locked and you look at notifications on your lock screen, you will notice that the notifications present the most basic information, such as that you received a text message from someone (Figure 17.1). If you have Face ID enabled and you look at your notifications, they will change when Face ID recognizes you to show you more detail. Here is an example of this: if you receive a text message from John Doe and you glance at your lock screen, you will see a notification that says: Messages, John Doe, Text Message. Now if you look directly at your iPhone's screen and you have Face ID enabled, after a moment Face ID will recognize your face and the notification will change to show you the contents of the text message. The same goes for other notifications as well. You can customize this feature in Settings -> Notifications -> Show Previews.

The Notification Center

At any time, you can view all your current notifications by accessing the Notification Center. To do this, tap down at the very top of your screen at the middle and swipe your finger down. This is your Notification Center (Figure 17.3). Here you can see all the notifications that you have not acknowledged, and they will be grouped by app. To view a set of notifications for an app, tap on it. To go directly to a particular notification, simply tap on it. To clear out a section of notifications, tap the small x next to it, and then tap clear. Simply perform the Go Home action to return to your home screen.

To open the
Notification Center,
tap down at the
very top of your
screen, at the
middle, and swipe
down.

Tap to clear the set
of notifications.

Tap and swipe to
the right to
quickly open the
notification (or
just tap on the
notification).

Tap and swipe to
the left to see some
options. Swiping
completely to the
left will clear the
notification.

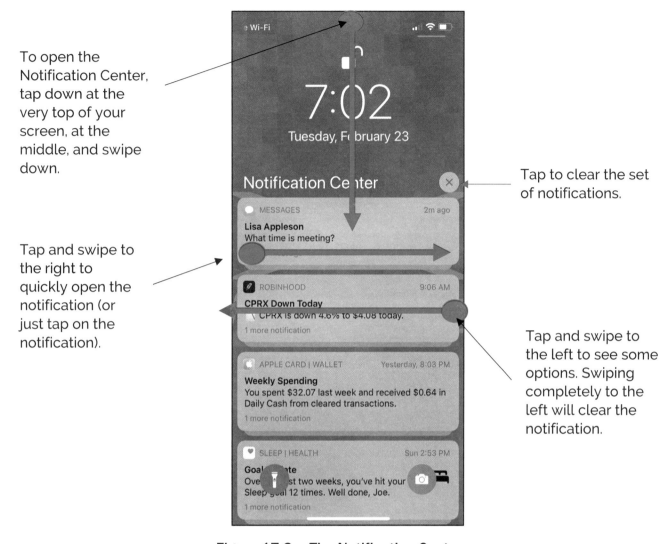

Figure 17.3 – The Notification Center

Examples of Notifications

As stated earlier, a notification can be from any app. For instance, a breaking news story from Fox News
can be a notification if you have the Fox News app. A new Facebook like on your post can be a notification
if you have the Facebook app installed. Basically, any app can deliver notifications.

Managing Notifications

Sometimes, you may not want to get notifications from a certain app, particularly if that app is prone to spamming you with useless notifications. These can be easily managed in the Settings app.

1. Open the Settings app.
2. Tap Notifications.
3. Tap the *app* you want to manage notifications for.
4. Now you can choose whether you want to allow notifications from this app. You can also choose the type of notification as well as some other options. (Figure 17.4)

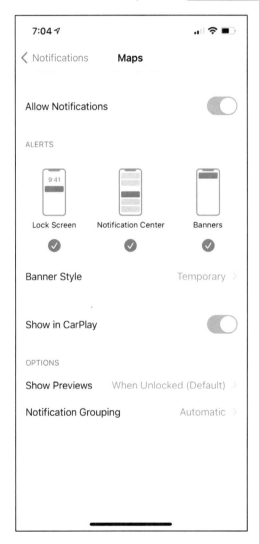

Figure 17.4 – Settings -> Notifications -> App Name (Maps app)

Chapter 18 – The Control Center

The Control Center, sometimes referred to as the "control panel," is a nifty tool on the iPhone that allows you to quickly change some settings. Let us explore it.

To Access the Control Center

1. To access the Control Center:
    a. **[iPhones without Home Button]:** On any screen on your iPhone, tap down at <u>the top right corner of your screen</u> and swipe straight down. This will bring up the Control Center (<u>Figure 18.1</u>).
    b. **[iPhones with Home Button]:** On any screen on your iPhone, tap down at the very bottom of your screen and swipe up. You will now see the Control Center (<u>Figure 18.1</u>). (Note: If you have iOS 10 on your iPhone, the Control Center will look a little bit different, but most of the same functions will be available to you.)

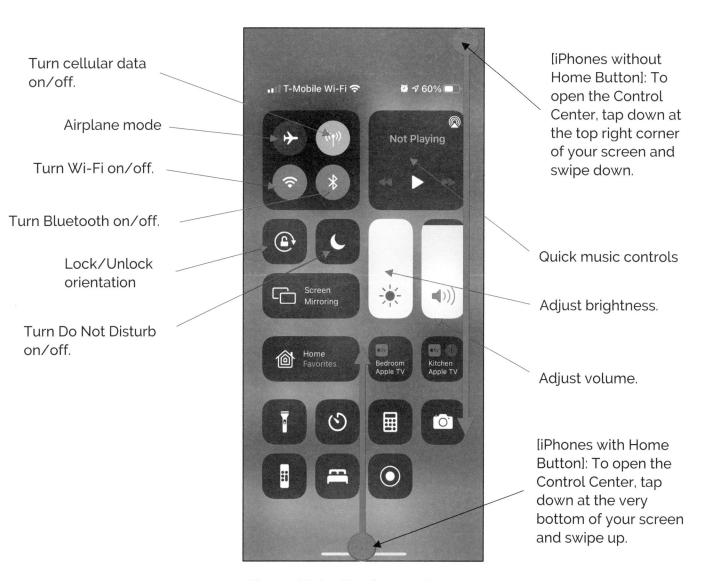

Turn cellular data on/off.

Airplane mode

Turn Wi-Fi on/off.

Turn Bluetooth on/off.

Lock/Unlock orientation

Turn Do Not Disturb on/off.

[iPhones without Home Button]: To open the Control Center, tap down at the top right corner of your screen and swipe down.

Quick music controls

Adjust brightness.

Adjust volume.

[iPhones with Home Button]: To open the Control Center, tap down at the very bottom of your screen and swipe up.

<u>Figure 18.1</u> – The Control Center

Control Center Functions

Inside your Control Center you will see some buttons. Tapping these buttons turns the selected setting on or off.

- **Airplane Mode** – Tapping on the airplane button turns airplane mode on or off. When a button is highlighted that means it is currently enabled. Airplane mode turns off all communication abilities on the iPhone, including cellular, Wi-Fi, and Bluetooth. Once you turn airplane mode on, you can still enable Wi-Fi by using the Control Center.
- **Wi-Fi** – The radio waves is the Wi-Fi button. Tapping this will turn Wi-Fi on or off.
- **Cellular Data** – The antenna icon enables or disables cellular data.
- **Bluetooth** – The Bluetooth button turns Bluetooth on or off. To connect to a Bluetooth device, you need to go to Settings -> Bluetooth.
- **Lock Portrait Orientation** – The lock orientation button will lock the orientation of your iPhone in portrait mode. When this is enabled, turning your iPhone to landscape orientation will not re-orientate the screen. If your iPhone's screen is not orientating to landscape mode, this option may be on.
- **Do Not Disturb** – The moon button enables or disables Do Not Disturb mode. When you enable Do Not Disturb mode, you will not receive notifications or hear any sounds for phone calls and messages when your screen is off. These along with all other notifications besides your alarm clock will be silenced.
- **Screen Mirroring** – This button lets you mirror your iPhone's screen to an Apple TV.

On the right side of the Control Center are two vertical ovals for brightness and volume. You can adjust these settings by tapping in the oval and dragging up or down to increase or decrease the brightness or volume.

Music Controls

The Music box in the Control Center allows you to quickly control your music. While a track is playing, you can bring up the Control Center and then use the skip back, pause/play, and skip forward icons to quickly navigate through your music without having to open the Music app. You can also bring up more options such as broadcasting to a Bluetooth connected speaker by tapping on the sound wave icon at the upper right of the Music box. Simply tap out of the enlarged Music box to return to the main Control Center.

Control Center Apps

The bottom rows of buttons in the Control Center open certain apps or perform functions.

- **Flashlight** – Tapping on the flashlight icon turns on your iPhone's flashlight, which is just the flash on your camera. Tap the flashlight again to turn it off. This function is very useful.
- **Timer/Alarm Clock** – The clock icon opens the Clock app and brings you directly to the Timer tab. In the Timer tab, you can set a timer that will notify you when the desired time elapses with an alert and sound. You can also set your alarm clock from here by tapping on the Alarm tab at the bottom. To create a new alarm, tap the plus icon at the upper right. Alternatively, you can enable a previously created alarm by tapping the small oval next to a time. You can now set the time for

your alarm and specify which type of alert you want. Tap <u>Save</u> at the upper right to finish setting the alarm.

- **Calculator** – The third icon at the bottom is the Calculator app. Tap this to open the calculator utility.
- **Camera** – The camera icon at the bottom opens the Camera app.
- **Other apps** – You may have additional buttons in your Control Center that will open other apps or perform certain app functions.

Haptic Touch Functions in the Control Center

You can use Haptic Touch on many of the Control Center buttons. As a reminder, Haptic Touch is pressing down on the screen and holding until you feel a haptic vibration. Three Haptic Touch examples are worth noting in the Control Center:

- **Night Shift** – To enable Night Shift, press on and hold the <u>vertical brightness adjustor</u> until you feel the haptic vibration and the adjustor comes to full screen. Underneath the adjustor will be the <u>Night Shift</u> button, which you can tap on to enable. When you turn Night Shift on, your iPhone will change its color display. The purpose of Night Shift is for when you are using your iPhone late at night and do not want your iPhone's screen straining your eyes and potentially keeping you awake. Night Shift will automatically turn off the next morning.
- **Dark Mode** – You can access Dark Mode in the same way you accessed Night Shift. Dark Mode changes the color scheme of your iPhone to dark. When enabled, the color scheme of various apps will be black instead of white (i.e., Messages app, Stocks app, etc.)
- **Flashlight** – Performing a Haptic Touch on the <u>flashlight button</u> allows you to adjust the power of the flashlight. Simply tap or drag your finger on the scale to adjust the power.
- **Time Do Not Disturb** – Performing a Haptic Touch on the <u>moon icon</u> will bring up timed options for Do Not Disturb. Now you can set a time for how long you want Do Not Disturb enabled.

Exiting the Control Center

Perform the <u>Go Home</u> action to exit the Control Center.

Adding Buttons to the Control Center

You can add or remove which buttons appear in the bottom row of the Control Center, and even create several rows of buttons. Here is how:

1. Open the <u>Settings</u> app.
2. Tap <u>Control Center</u>.
3. On the following screen, you can remove buttons by tapping the <u>red minus symbol</u> next to a function, and add buttons by tapping the <u>green plus symbol</u> (<u>Figure 18.2</u>).

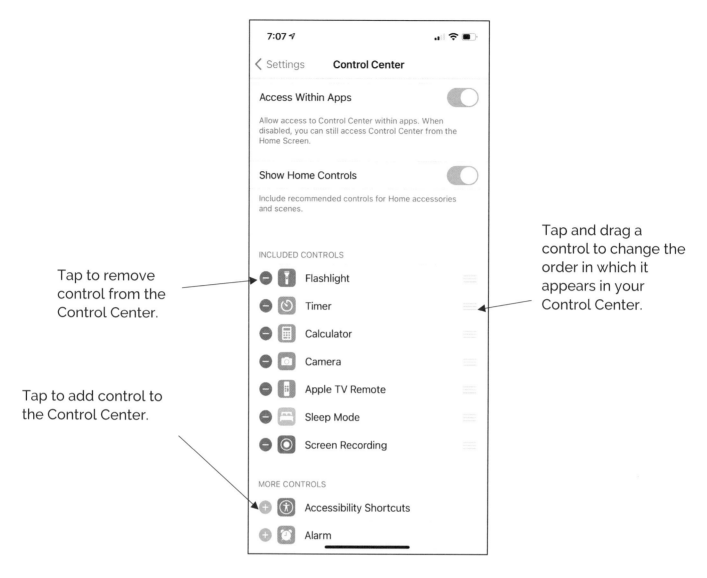

Figure 18.2 – Settings -> Control Center

Chapter 19 – Siri

Siri, as you may have heard, is Apple's intelligent voice assistant. You can talk to Siri, and Siri will listen to what you say and try to do whatever you ask. The possibilities of what you can do with Siri are endless.

Turning Siri On

By default, Siri is enabled on your iPhone. To be sure, let us make sure Siri is enabled. To do this, follow these steps (Figure 19.1):

1. Open Settings.
2. Find and tap Siri & Search (Or just Siri for iOS 10).
3. Make sure Press Side Button for Siri **[iPhones without Home Button]** or Press Home for Siri **[iPhones with Home Button]** is enabled at the top. (The slider tab next to it should be green. If not, tap it.)

Figure 19.1 – Settings -> Siri & Search

While we are in the Siri settings screen, let us take a quick look at some of the settings you can adjust.

- **Allow Siri When Locked –** Allows you to access Siri when your iPhone is locked. I usually leave this enabled so I can access Siri quickly without unlocking my iPhone.
- **Listen for "Hey Siri" –** With this enabled, you can access Siri by simply saying "Hey Siri" at any time. If your vehicle has Apple CarPlay, you will need this enabled.
- **Other Settings –** The settings at the bottom allow you to change some other settings including which language you want Siri to use and which voice you want Siri to have.

Accessing Siri

Now that Siri is enabled on your iPhone, let us go back to the home screen. From the home screen accessing Siri is very easy. The easiest way to access Siri is to press and hold the sleep/wake button **[iPhones without Home Button]** or press or hold the home button **[iPhones with Home Button]** until you see a sound wave appear at the bottom of your screen (Figure 19.2).

You can make Siri start listening again by pressing on the sound wave (or this icon shown), or pressing and holding the sleep/wake button / home button again.

Figure 19.2 – Using Siri

Using Siri

Now let us try some examples to see exactly how Siri works. First, let me note that when you access Siri by holding the power/home button, you have two different approaches. One is, when the sound wave appears, you can let go of the power/home button and start speaking. Two is, when the sound wave appears, you can continue holding down on the power/home button, start speaking, and release the power/home button when you are done speaking. Either way works. For simplicity, I am going to use the former method in our examples. Keep in mind you can also access Siri by speaking "Hey Siri".

So, let us press and hold the power/home button until the sound wave appears then release the power/home button. Now we can say, "What is the weather?" Siri will listen, then respond with some information. She can either speak the information back to you or bring up a screen with the information you requested. To start a new Siri session or attempt to speak again, tap on the graphic that appears at the bottom of your screen or just hold the power/home button again.

Let us try another example, press and hold the power/home button and release, and then say, "Show me my Photos." Siri will listen and then automatically open the Photos app for you.

There are countless things you can say to Siri that she will perform. Try out anything you would like. A few more examples are listed below, and you can see a much larger list of examples in the appendix of this text.

- Make Phone Calls – "Call *Contact Name*"
- Lookup Contact Information – "Lookup *Contact Name*"
- Lookup Sports Scores – "Who won the White Sox game today?"
- Set an Alarm Clock – "Set an alarm for 6:30 AM"
- Do Math – "What is two plus two?"
- Visit Websites – "Bring me to Infinity Guides dot com."

Chapter 20 – Native Apps

Let us explore some native apps that come preloaded on the iPhone. Many of these are very useful and you may find yourself using them often.

Music

The Music app is where you can play and listen to your music. There are three ways to listen to music. The first is to load songs that you already own onto your iPhone. To do this, you will need to either use your Mac or a Windows computer with iTunes software. To see how to do this, go to www.infinityguides.com and search for 'iTunes' at the top.

The second way to listen to music is to use the Apple Music service. This service lets you listen to nearly any song you want at any time, right from your iPhone, any computer, or device. The Apple Music service is huge and is a subscription service from Apple. To learn how to use Apple Music, go to www.infinityguides.com and search for 'Apple Music'.

The third way is to purchase and download music from the iTunes Store app on your iPhone or through iTunes on a computer. Once you purchase and download music, it will automatically appear in the Music app.

Once you have music on your iPhone using any of the above methods, using the Music app is straight-forward. You can browse through the app using the tabs at the bottom, and simply tap on a song to play it. You can also quickly skip through tracks in the Control Center, which is covered in Chapter 18.

Maps

The Maps app is a great app for turn-by-turn navigation. In other words, it is a GPS right on your iPhone (Figure 20.1). Inside the Maps app you can tap into the search bar and type in the address of where you want to go. You can also search for nearby places. While typing an address or place, Maps will present suggestions as to what you are looking for. If what you are looking for comes up, you can tap on it.

Tap on Directions to get driving directions to the location. Your iPhone will give you turn-by-turn directions as you are driving. Furthermore, the Maps app works great with vehicles that have Apple CarPlay.

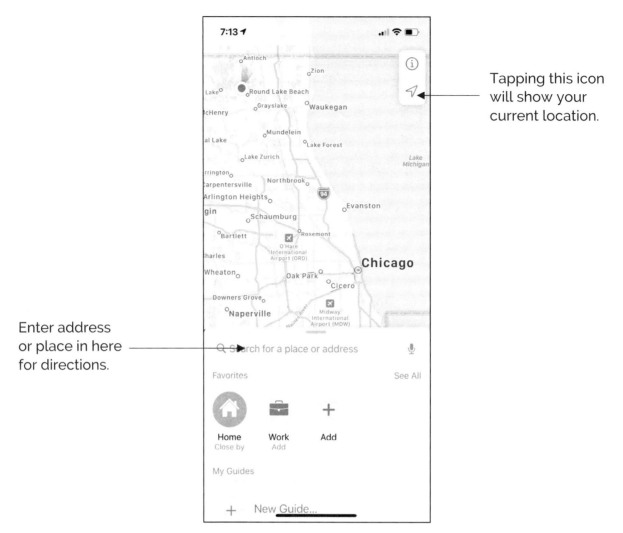

Tapping this icon will show your current location.

Enter address or place in here for directions.

Figure 20.1 – Maps App

Note: There are other apps that offer GPS and turn-by-turn directions. Two popular ones are Google Maps and Waze, available in the App Store for free.

Weather

The Weather app is a very simple app that shows you the current weather and forecast. By default, the Weather app will show you your current location's weather if you have Location Services enabled in Settings.

To add an area to the Weather app, tap the 3 bulleted lines at the bottom right. Now tap on the magnifying glass (search symbol) and then you can enter a postal code to quickly add that area to your Weather app. You can browse through your different saved locations by swiping left or right. You can also scroll up and down to see additional weather information. (Figure 20.2)

Figure 20.2 – Weather App

Tap here to add another location to check weather.

FaceTime
(See Figure 20.3)

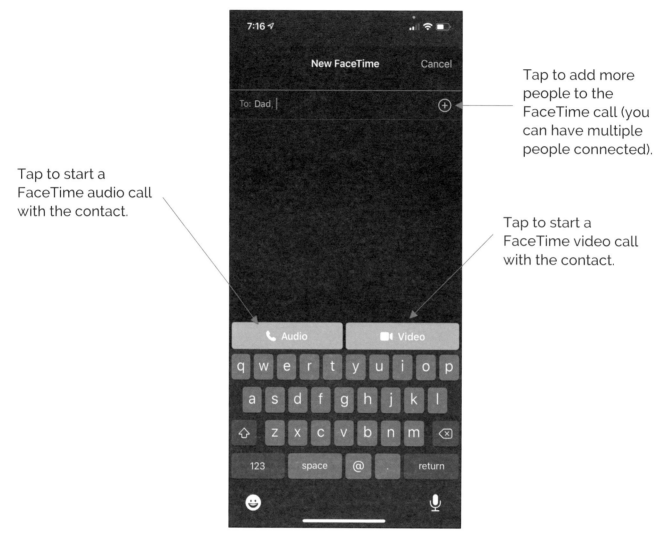

Tap to add more people to the FaceTime call (you can have multiple people connected).

Tap to start a FaceTime audio call with the contact.

Tap to start a FaceTime video call with the contact.

Figure 20.3 – FaceTime App

FaceTime, which I have mentioned briefly earlier in this text, is an app that allows you to partake in video calls with other Apple users. When you open FaceTime, you can place a video call by tapping on the plus sign at the upper right. Now you can search through your contacts for someone to FaceTime with. As you are typing a contact name, suggestions will appear below. If a suggestion appears in blue text, this means that you can partake in a FaceTime call with that person. If the text is grey, then you cannot FaceTime with them. Alternatively, you can look through your contact list using the + icon. When you have found the person you want to FaceTime with, tap on their _name_. Now FaceTime will determine if they are able to make a FaceTime call. You will know if you are able to FaceTime that person by looking at the Audio and Video boxes near the middle of your screen. If the boxes are green, then you can FaceTime with this person. (Figure 20.3). If they are greyed out, then you cannot FaceTime with them. When both icons are greyed out, that usually means that the person does not have FaceTime on their device. You can also add additional people to the FaceTime call before initiating it. In other words, you can video chat with multiple people at once.

FaceTime calls have some interesting controls you can utilize. You can change which camera you are using (selfie or regular) by tapping on the camera flip icon during the call. You can also add special effects to the FaceTime call by tapping on the effects icon. Some special effects include animated face, text on the screen, and more. (Figure 20.4)

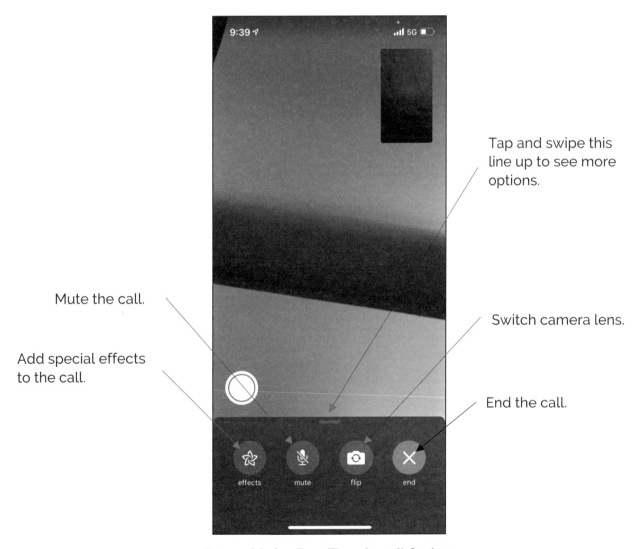

Figure 20.4 – FaceTime In-call Options

Clock

We have already covered some of the Clock app in Chapter 18. There are a few things we missed however, so we will cover them now. In this app you can see the time around the world, as well as set an alarm (Figure 20.5), and start a timer. You can also use the stopwatch function by tapping on the Stopwatch tab at the bottom. Lastly, the <u>Bedtime</u> tab allows you to set up a custom bedtime and wake-up alarm, depending upon how you sleep.

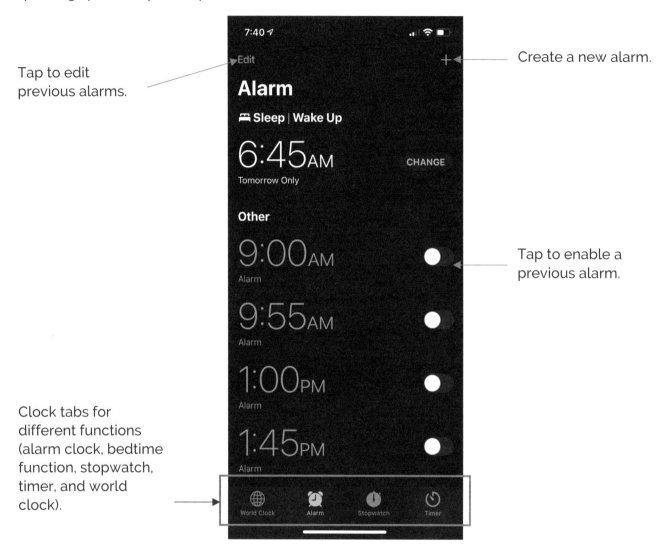

Tap to edit previous alarms.

Create a new alarm.

Tap to enable a previous alarm.

Clock tabs for different functions (alarm clock, bedtime function, stopwatch, timer, and world clock).

<u>Figure 20.5</u> – Clock App (Alarm Tab)

Notes

The Notes app is an incredibly useful app for creating notes. It is very easy to use; just open the <u>Notes</u> app, tap the <u>pencil and square icon</u> at the lower right to start a new note, and begin typing away. Notes save automatically, and you can access all your saved notes in the main notes screen (use the <u>back arrows</u> at the upper left). You can delete notes by tapping on the <u>circle with three dots icon</u> at the upper right. (<u>Figure 20.6</u>)

Furthermore, while creating a note you can sketch and use additional tools by using the icons at the bottom of your screen. You can also password protect certain notes by opening the note, tapping the <u>three dots in a circle</u> at the upper right, and then tapping <u>Lock</u>.

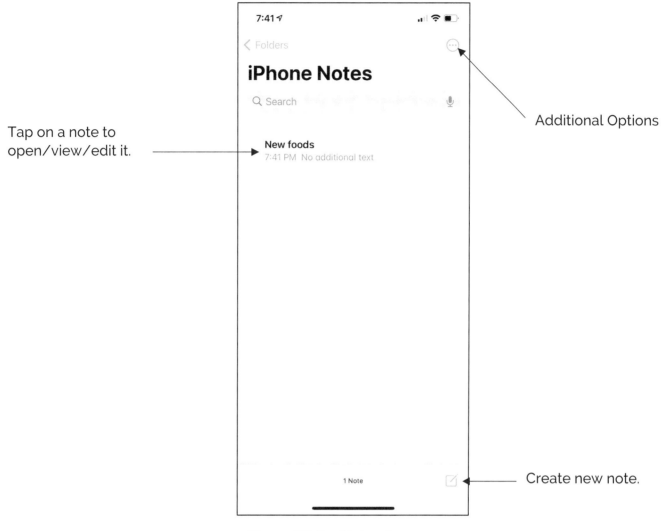

Figure 20.6 – Notes App

Calendar

The Calendar app is a simple app that allows you to create events and reminders. To view all the events you have on a day, simply tap on that day.

To Create a New Event (See Figure 20.7)

1. Tap the plus icon at the upper right.
2. Enter in all the corresponding information, if required. Include the date and time (if applicable).
3. Choose whether you want to set an alarm to remind you about this event.
4. When you are done, tap Add at the upper right.
5. Your event has now been added to your calendar.

You can tell if you have scheduled events on a day if a dot appears below the date. You can tap on Today at the lower right to be brought to your current day, which shows you your daily schedule.

You can also see a quick view of what you have coming up on your calendar from the home screen. Simply go to your home screen and swipe your finger to the right until you get to the Today View. If you have any events in your calendar coming up, they will appear here.

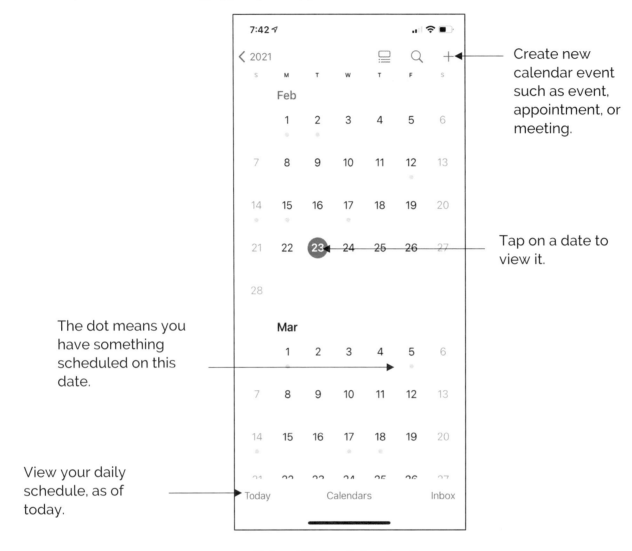

Figure 20.7 – Calendar App

Chapter 21 – Tips & Tricks

Congratulations! You have made it through most of this book, and you should now have a solid understanding of how to use your iPhone. There are no more "basics" left to teach you, so I will leave you with a few tips and tricks that you may find helpful when using your iPhone.

Backing up your Device

This is a MAJOR tip. You should always have a backup of your iPhone's data available in case anything happens. If you destroy or lose your iPhone, a backup will allow you to get all your data back. There are two ways to back up your device.

Method One: Back up to iCloud (Recommended)

Backing up to iCloud is the best way to go. This is done automatically and continuously so you never have to worry about anything. You will need an Apple ID to do so, and you must be signed into iCloud with that Apple ID (covered in Chapter 5). To turn iCloud backup on, follow these steps:

1. Open Settings.
2. Tap the big box at the top with your name.
3. Tap iCloud.
4. Tap iCloud Backup.
5. Now make sure iCloud Backup is on (enabled green). If it was off previously, tap on Back Up Now to begin the backup.

When your iPhone is backing up to iCloud, you do not need to worry about setting up backup again, as your iPhone will backup periodically, usually when you are sleeping and your iPhone is charging. Please note your iPhone must be connected to Wi-Fi to initiate its automatic backup. Now should anything ever happen to your iPhone, you can always get your data back. iCloud saves your data securely in the cloud.

Method Two: Back up to Mac or Windows PC with iTunes

The second way to back up your device is to either use your Mac, or a Windows PC with iTunes. Doing this saves a backup on your computer that can quickly be restored. To learn how to do this, visit www.infinityguides.com and search for 'iTunes'.

Taking a Screenshot

A screenshot is a picture of exactly what your screen looks like and can be very useful. For instance, say you received a text with instructions on how to bake a cake, and you want to share those instructions with a friend via text message. One way to accomplish this is take a screenshot of the original text and send the picture of that screenshot to your friend.

At any time, you can take a screenshot of what you are viewing on your iPhone. Here is how:

[iPhones without Home Button]: To take a screenshot, press the power button and the volume up button at the same time and then release.

[iPhones with Home Button]: To take a screenshot, press and hold the <u>power button</u> and the <u>home button</u> at the same time for about one second, and then release.

You will know a screenshot was taken when you see your screen flash, and the screenshot appears in the lower corner of your screen. You can tap on the picture to view it, and several sharing and editing features will become available to you. Screenshots will save as pictures in your Photos app.

Background Apps & the App Switcher

(See <u>Figure 21.1</u>) Whenever you open an app, it remains open in the background even after you leave the app. In some circumstances, it can be beneficial to completely close an app running in the background if it is not working properly. You can also use this method to quickly go to an app you were recently using.

[iPhones with Home Button]: To access the App Switcher, simply double press the <u>home button</u> quickly.

[iPhones without Home Button]: To access the App Switcher, perform a home swipe BUT do not lift your finger off the screen. Instead, leave your finger on your screen at the end of the home swipe for an additional moment, and then release your finger.

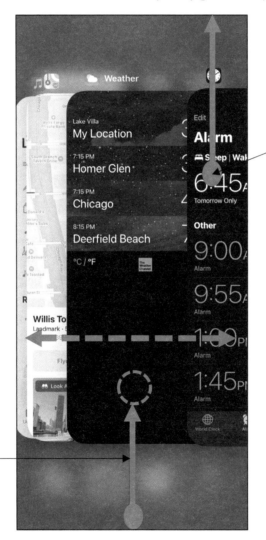

You can completely shut down an app down by tapping on an app's screen and swiping it up and off the screen. You can even swipe off every background app running for a "clean slate". Furthermore, you can shut down multiple apps at once using multiple fingers.

Figure 21.1 – Accessing the App Switcher

How to Close Background Apps OR Go to a Recent App

1. Accessing the App Switcher is different depending upon which iPhone you have:
   a. **[iPhones without Home Button]:** Perform a <u>home swipe</u> but DO NOT lift your finger off the

screen at the end. Instead, leave your finger on your screen near the middle for an extra moment or until you see an app screen appear at the left. You can now release your finger. Your home screen should break away and you should see numerous screens next to each other. (If it did not work, try again. This gesture can require some practice.) (Figure 21.1)

   b. **[iPhones with Home Button]:** Double press the home button quickly. Your home screen should break away and you should see numerous screens next to each other.

2. If you want to quickly go to another app you used recently, swipe left or right and tap on the screen of the app you want to go to.

3. To shut down an app, tap on any app screen and swipe it up and off the screen. This shuts down an app completely.

4. Perform the Go Home action to return when done.

TIP: If an app is not working properly or is frozen, the quickest way to fix it is to completely shut the app down by using the App Switcher and then re-opening it.

Restart your iPhone

It is a good practice to restart your iPhone every now and then, the same way you would restart a computer to keep it fresh. I recommend restarting your iPhone if it is running slow or not working properly. Doing so can fix the problem. As a good practice, I recommend restarting your iPhone at least once every two months. To restart your iPhone, shut it down and then wait 60 seconds after the phone is off before you power it back on.

Copy and Paste

We have already covered how to copy a picture. As a reminder, you can do this by using a Haptic Touch on a photo thumbnail, and then tapping Copy. Alternatively, you can tap on the square and pencil icon and then tap Copy. To paste it in text somewhere, double tap with your finger in the text area, and then tap on Paste.

To copy and paste text, find the text you want to copy and tap and hold on it. Now move the small marker dots left and right by tapping and dragging them to select the exact portion of text you want to copy. Now tap the Copy box. You can paste the text by double tapping in a text box and then tapping Paste. (Figure 21.2)

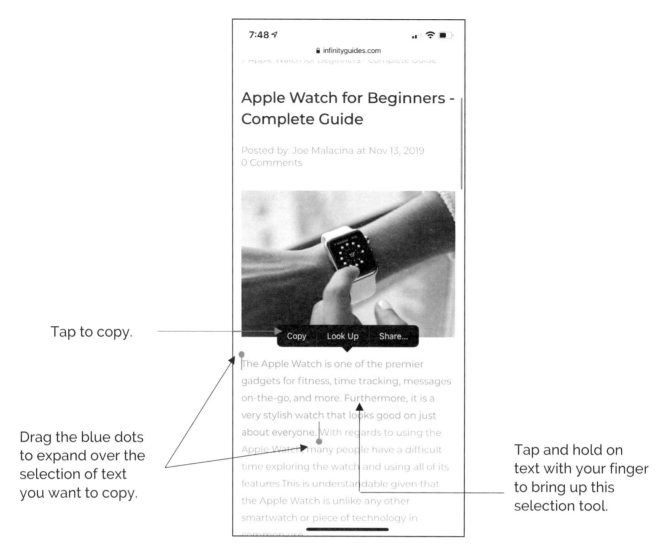

Tap to copy.

Drag the blue dots
to expand over the
selection of text
you want to copy.

Tap and hold on
text with your finger
to bring up this
selection tool.

Figure 21.2 – Copy and Paste Text

Low Power Mode

There are some things you can do to improve the battery life of your iPhone. The biggest way to preserve your battery life is by switching on Low Power Mode, which reduces power consumption temporarily. Low Power Mode is an excellent feature to use when your battery is running low and you cannot afford for your battery to die anytime soon. To enable it, follow these steps:

1. Open Settings.
2. Tap Battery.
3. Tap the oval box next to Low Power Mode to enable it.
4. Tap the oval box again to turn it back off.

Personal Hotspot

Your iPhone can become a personal hotspot, which in layman's terms is a device which can broadcast its internet connection to other devices. Using the personal hotspot feature is limited by your cellular provider, and some providers charge to use this service. So, before you enable your personal hotspot, check with your cellular provider.

To enable the personal hotspot:

1. Open Settings.
2. Tap Personal Hotspot.
3. Enable Personal Hotspot by tapping on the tabular icon next to Allow others to Join. When the tab is green, personal hotspot is enabled.
4. Set a Wi-Fi password for devices to access your personal hotspot by tapping in the Wi-Fi Password box and creating a password.

A personal hotspot is a great way to create a Wi-Fi network for your other devices when Wi-Fi is not available. Be sure to turn Personal Hotspot off when you are done, as it uses significant battery power and data.

Screen Time

Screen Time is a nifty feature that allows you to see how you are using your iPhone. You can use this feature to see which apps you use the most, and how much time you spend on those apps. Using Screen Time is straight forward. To access Screen Time:

1. Open Settings.
2. Tap Screen Time
3. Now you can see data and statistics of your iPhone usage. You can tap on any information to see more details.

You can also use Screen Time to set up parental controls on other devices that you manage. To learn how to do this, visit www.infinityguides.com and search for "parental controls".

Messages App FaceTime

You can quickly create a FaceTime call with someone you have shared a text message conversation with through the Messages app. You can even use this tip to quickly create a group FaceTime call with an entire group thread in the Messages app. To do this:

1. Open the Messages app.
2. Open the *thread* that you want to start a FaceTime call with. It can even be a group thread.
3. Inside the thread, tap on the *name of the thread* at the top.
4. Tap the FaceTime icon.
5. You will now commence a FaceTime call with everyone in the thread.

QuickPath

A nice feature of the iPhone is the ability to use swipe-to-text, which is called QuickPath. This allows you to use your keyboard to swipe-to-text instead of typing each letter of each word individually. Here is how it works:

1. Bring up the keyboard on your iPhone, such as when using the Messages app.

2. Now you can use the keyboard normally, or you can use QuickPath.
3. Let us say you want to type the message "Hello, how are you?" Normally, you would have to type each letter of each word individually.
4. Instead, you can **swipe** quickly to each letter and not have to remove your finger from the screen to complete a word.
    a. To type in the word "Hello": Tap on the letter **H**, but do not remove your finger from the screen.
    b. Drag or "swipe" your finger to the letter **e**, then drag your finger to the letter **l,** then pause for a moment on the letter **l** to indicate that there are two L's in a row, then finally drag your finger to the letter **o**, and then release your finger. (<u>Figure 21.3</u>)
    c. Your iPhone will enter the word **Hello** for you.
    d. You can repeat the process for the rest of the message.

If your iPhone types the wrong word, you can quickly change it by tapping on one of the suggestions.

Enter the word "hello" by dragging your finger to each letter of "hello" while remaining on the screen, without having to tap each letter individually.

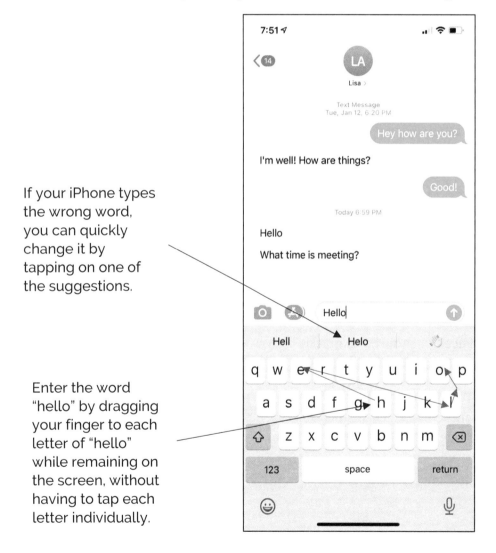

<u>Figure 21.3</u> – **QuickPath Texting**

iMessage Profile

Another feature on the iPhone is the ability to create a profile for yourself in the Messages app. This profile is commonly called your iMessage profile, and it allows you to set your name and profile picture that other Apple devices users will see when messaging you.

To set this up, follow these steps:

1. Open the Messages app.
2. Tap on Edit at the upper left.
3. Tap on Edit Name and Photo.
4. Now you will be able to edit your display name and display photo for text messages. For your photo, you can choose one you have saved in your Photos app or create a Memoji or Animoji, which are digital avatars of yourself.
5. You can also choose who you want to share your iMessage profile with. Contacts Only will share your profile with all your contacts who have an Apple device. In other words, they will be able to see your display name and photo automatically when you begin messaging with them. If you choose Always Ask, you will get to manually decide who sees your iMessage profile. (Figure 21.4)

When you use the "Always Ask" option for sharing your name and photo, you will be prompted for each thread you are a part of on whether you want to share your name and photo with everyone in the thread.

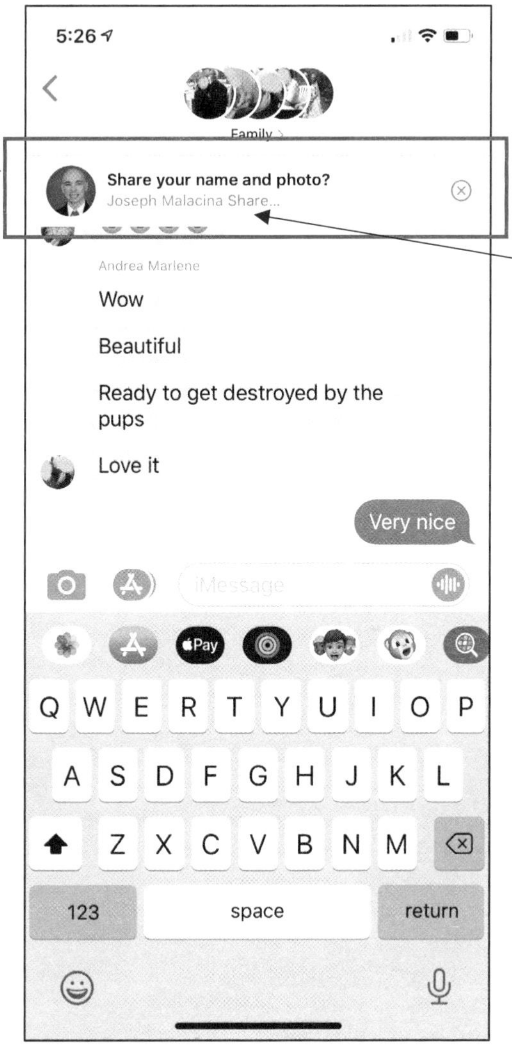

Tap on Share... to share your name and photo with everyone in the thread.

When you share your name and photo (iMessage profile) with someone, your name in their contact list will be updated to reflect the information you shared. The same goes if someone were to share their iMessage profile with you.

Figure 21.4 – Sharing your Name and Photo with someone you are Messaging (Always Ask option)

Only people who have Apple devices can share their iMessage profiles.

Siri Easter Eggs

As mentioned in the Siri chapter, you can say anything you want to Siri. Anything. You may even discover some Easter eggs while speaking to her. Try these:

- How much wood could a woodchuck chuck is a woodchuck could chuck wood?
- What do you look like?
- I love my iPhone.

Try some more yourself.

Chapter 22 – Conclusion & More Resources

Thank you for taking the time to read this book. It is my hope that you feel much better and confident about using your iPhone. I am personally confident that if you took the time to read this entire book, then you will have no problem using every aspect of your iPhone with ease. Continue to use this book as a reference when you need it. The table of contents can quickly lead you to your answer, and the appendixes can be especially helpful as well, and I hope you use them.

I welcome your thoughts and feedback on this text, please come visit my Facebook page online at www.facebook.com/joemalacina1. You can also tweet me @JoeMalacina on Twitter. I am often online answering questions from people who have read this text and helping people with complex iPhone issues. As a last piece of advice, please remember your Apple ID, Apple ID password, and lock screen passcode. Forgetting even one of these, especially your lock screen passcode, can be a real headache.

Enjoy using your iPhone!

More Resources

This guide has covered all the beginner aspects of the iPhone. We have also covered many intermediate and advanced aspects, but there is still plenty more you can learn. Most notably, there is a lot to learn about specific apps. You can also learn more about Apple Music, iTunes, and social media on your iPhone.

Infinity Guides is an excellent resource for beginners, and on the Infinity Guides website you can find books, manuals, DVDs, and online courses made for beginners. The online courses can be especially helpful as most of them are about 30 minutes long and teach you through video instruction. I have created a short list of things you can learn with Infinity Guides for your reference.

www.infinityguides.com **Content:**

- *Facebook for Beginners*
- *Twitter for Beginners*
- *Apple Music for Beginners*
- *Online Safety: The Complete Guide to Being Safe Online*
- *Smartphones & Tablets for Beginners*
- *Instagram App for Beginners*
- *Snapchat App for Beginners*
- *iTunes for Beginners*
- *Mac Computer for Beginners*
- *Making your Computer Fast Again Tutorial*
- *Kindle Manual for Beginners*
- *Fire HD Tablet Manual for Beginners*

APPENDIX A – Additional Recommended Apps

- **560 The Answer** – A talk radio station's app that allows you to listen live and listen later.
- **AirBnB** – Book lodging from regular people who put their vacation homes, rentals, condos, and dwellings up for short-term lodging.
- **Best Fiends** – Puzzle game
- **Bible** – App for reading the bible.
- **Bitmoji** – Fun app where you can create an emoji and avatar of yourself and share with friends. Works with the Messages app.
- **CARROT** – Quirky but powerful weather app
- **Crossword** – Crossword puzzle game app
- **Doordash** – Food delivery app
- **Dropbox** – File sharing and cloud app
- **Fox Sports** – Official app for the Fox Sports channel
- **Expedia** – Travel app that allows you to compare and book travel accommodations.
- **Facebook** – The Facebook social media app. Learn to use it at www.infinityguides.com
- **Facebook Messenger** – The messaging app for Facebook
- **Fandango** – Lookup movie show times, reviews, information, and local theaters
- **Flixster** – Movie ticketing app
- **Fox News** – The official app for the Fox News Channel
- **Brave** – Alternative web browser with enhanced security features
- **Groupon** – Shopping app where you can purchase discounts and special deals.
- **HD Wallpapers** – App for downloading wallpapers for your iPhone.
- **iHeartRadio** – Radio app where you can listen to radio stations across the world and internet.
- **Instagram** – Popular social media app for picture sharing. Learn to use it at www.infinityguides.com
- **McDonalds** – McDonald's official app which offers coupons and deals.
- **Microsoft Office** – Apps for Word, Excel, and other Microsoft Office products
- **MLB App** – Official Major League Baseball app
- **MyFitnessPal** – Dieting and fitness app.
- **MyRadar** – Weather app with detailed radar
- **Netflix** – Subscription app that allows you to watch TV shows and movies.
- **NFL App** – Official National Football League app
- **OpenTable** – Dining app that allows you to book reservations and read reviews.
- **Pages** – Word Processing app
- **Pinterest** – Popular social media app for shopping and ideas

- **Postmates** – App for ordering delivery and takeout food.
- **Radio.com** – Radio app that allows you to listen to various radio stations.
- **Robinhood** – Investing app
- **Shazam** – App that can listen to and identify most songs.
- **Shopular** – Shopping app that offers coupons and deals.
- **SitorSquat** – Miscellaneous app where you can quickly find a public bathroom and read user reviews of bathrooms.
- **Sky Guide** – Fun app to view star constellations.
- **Skype** – Video chat with your friends and family
- **Snapchat** – Social Media app especially popular among teens that allows you to send pictures and videos that disappear after a short time. Learn to use it at www.infinityguides.com
- **Speedtest** – App that allows you to test your internet speed.
- **SpotHero** – App that allows you to find and book parking.
- **Stitcher** – App that downloads podcasts and notifies you when they are available.
- **Target** – Shopping app for Target
- **The Weather Channel** – The always useful Weather Channel app
- **TheGrint** – Golf app with GPS and handicap tracker
- **TuneIn** – An excellent app for listening to radio stations and podcasts.
- **Twitch** – Video game streaming app where you can watch people play games.
- **Twitter** – Very popular social media app where users can "tweet" messages to the world and to their followers. Learn more at www.infinityguides.com
- **Uber** – Ride-sharing app
- **USPS Mobile** – USPS app where you can track your shipments and order postage.
- **Venmo** – Pay people with your phone.
- **VLC** – Video Player app
- **Wall Street Journal** – News app
- **Waze** – For Directions & GPS, with real-time traffic and user-generated alerts
- **WebMD** – Health app for viewing various health information.
- **Words with Friends** – A scrabble like game where you can compete with other people online.
- **Yelp** – An app for reading and posting reviews of various places such as restaurants.
- **Your Airline's App** – Download and present your boarding pass using your iPhone and check the status of your flight.
- **Your Bank's App** – Always a good idea to have your bank's app so you can check balances, make deposits, and perform other banking activities.

APPENDIX B – Siri Examples

These are all examples of things you can say to Siri.

- What time is it?
- Show me restaurants around here.
- Call *Contact Name*
- Send a text to *contact name.*
- Open *app name*
- Check my e-mail.
- Check my messages.
- Do I have any appointments today?
- Check my battery life.
- Send a text to *contact name.*
- Tell *contact name* I am on my way in a text.
- What movies are playing?
- Play *song name.*
- Play *playlist name.*
- Play *artist name.*
- Remind me to wash the dishes tonight.
- Email *contact name* about the trip
- Wake me up at 7 AM tomorrow.
- Note that I need to get my dog a new bone.
- Turn on Airplane mode.
- Decrease/Increase my brightness.
- What is Apple's stock price?
- What is the address of *contact name*?
- Change my wallpaper.
- Play a random song.
- Where can I get a burger around here?
- Find me a gas station.
- Shuffle my songs.
- What is the weather right now?
- Who is the current president of *country name*?

APPENDIX C – List of Common Functions

- **Add New Email to iPhone:** Settings -> Mail -> Accounts -> Add Account
- **Change Language:** Settings -> General -> Language & Region
- **Change Lock Screen Password:** Settings -> Face/Touch ID & Passcode
- **Change Ringtones:** Settings -> Sounds & Haptics
- **Change Wallpaper:** Settings -> Wallpapers
- **Check for iOS Updates:** Settings -> General -> Software Update
- **Completely Restore iPhone to Factory Default (WARNING: this will delete all your iPhone data and bring it back to right out of the box status. DO NOT DO THIS unless you know what you are doing and why.):** Settings -> General -> Reset -> Erase all Content and Settings - > enter passwords
- **Connect to a Bluetooth Device:** Settings -> Bluetooth -> My Devices
- **Connect to a Wi-Fi Network:** Settings -> Wi-Fi -> Tap on Network -> Enter password -> Tap Join
- **Create New Text:** Messages -> Square and Pencil Icon
- **Join Apple Music:** Settings -> Music -> Join Apple Music
- **Set Default Search Engine:** Settings -> Safari -> Search Engine
- **Clear Your Internet History:** Settings -> Safari -> Clear History and Website Data
- **Sign into your Apple ID:** Settings -> Big Box at top -> Apple ID
- **Switch to Military Time:** Settings -> General -> Date & Time -> 24 Hour Time
- **Turn Location Services On/Off:** Settings -> Privacy -> Location Services
- **Turn on Do Not Disturb:** Control Center -> Moon Icon
- **Turn on Dark Mode:** Control Center -> Haptic Touch on Brightness Slider -> Dark Mode
- **Turn on Night Shift:** Control Center -> Haptic Touch on Brightness Slider -> Night Shift
- **Turn on iCloud Photos:** Settings -> Photos -> iCloud Photos
- **Turn Siri On/Off:** Settings -> Siri & Search
- **Create a new E-mail:** Mail -> Square and Pencil Icon
- **Delete a Recent Call History:** Phone -> Recents Tab -> Swipe left over a recent call
- **Add Emoji to Keyboard:** Settings -> General -> Keyboard -> Keyboards -> Add New Keyboard... -> Emoji
- **Set an Alarm Clock:** Control Center -> Timer icon -> Alarm Tab
- **Add a Widget to Home Screen:** Tap and Hold Home Screen -> Plus Symbol (upper left)
- **Forgot Your Passcode?:** Go to https://support.apple.com/en-us/HT204306
- **Forgot your Apple ID password?** Go to https://support.apple.com/en-us/HT201487

Check out more beginner's guides and manuals at:

www.infinityguides.com

Index